Important Information

BEFORE I DIE

End of life Planner, Workbook,
Organizer and Journal

1st Echo Publishing

CONTENTS

———

WELCOME   **5**

QUICK START GUIDE   **7**

PART 1: EXPLANATION (PERSON 1)   **10**

PART 1: INDIVIDUAL INFORMATION (Person 1)   **19**

    Chapter 1: FINANCIAL INFORMATION   39

    Chapter 2: HEALTH & MEDICAL INFORMATION   80

    Chapter 3: MEDICATIONS TO-GO PAGE   91

    Chapter 4: PASSWORDS & PROTECTED INFORMATION   94

    Chapter 5: LEGAL DOCUMENTS & INFORMATION   104

    Chapter 6: IMPORTANT CONTACTS   112

    Chapter 7: IMPORTANT RESOURCES   115

    Chapter 8: TO-DO LIST   132

    Chapter 9: THOUGHTS & FINAL WISHES   137

PART 2: EXPLANATION (PERSON 2)   **144**

PART 2: INDIVIDUAL INFORMATION (Person 2)   **153**

Chapter 10: FINANCIAL INFORMATION   172

Chapter 11: HEALTH & MEDICAL INFORMATION   215

Chapter 12: MEDICATIONS TO-GO PAGE   226

Chapter 13: PASSWORDS & PROTECTED INFORMATION   229

Chapter 14: LEGAL DOCUMENTS & INFORMATION   239

Chapter 15: IMPORTANT CONTACTS   247

Chapter 16: IMPORTANT RESOURCES   250

Chapter 17: TO-DO LIST   266

Chapter 18: THOUGHTS & FINAL WISHES   271

CONCLUSION   **278**

WELCOME

———

This is a journal designed to assist husband and wife or life partners in organizing and storing vital information in one convenient location. The paperback version has spaces to add this key information, while the Ebook can still be a purchase option for people that want to add this information to another source. Use this book as an all inclusive guide.

It's easy to let important details slip through the cracks in the hustle and bustle of daily life. Keeping track of your finances, legal documents, health, and final wishes can all seem overwhelming. However, with this journal, you and your partner will be able to stay on top of everything and be prepared for whatever life throws at you.

The goal of this journal is to provide a comprehensive resource for documenting and organizing critical information in the event of an emergency. You can ensure that your loved ones won't have to scramble to find the details they need during a stressful and emotional time by collecting all of the necessary information in one place.

The advantages of keeping your information organized and current are immeasurable. You and your partner can make informed decisions about your finances, health, and end-of-life wishes if you take the time to fill out this journal together. Furthermore, having a clear plan in place can provide peace of mind and reduce stress during trying times.

This journal is a one-stop-shop for all of your essential information, with easy-to-use sections covering everything from personal profiles to important contacts, financial information to health records, and even final wishes and arrangements.

You probably share many aspects of your life as husband and wife. You may have joint bank accounts, jointly owned property, or health insurance policies that cover both of you. While this can help to simplify some aspects of your life, it can also make it more difficult to organize important information.

By combining your information in this journal, you can easily keep track of all of the details that are important to both of you. You'll have a clear picture of your joint financial situation, know who to call in an emergency, and be able to locate important documents such as your will or power of attorney with ease.

However, this journal isn't just for sharing information; it also allows you to record your personal preferences and wishes. You will each have your own section to fill out, where you will be able to list important contacts, financial information, and legal documents that are unique to you. This ensures that each of you is in control of your own affairs and can make informed decisions based on your individual needs and desires.

The peace of mind that this journal provides is one of its most significant advantages. Knowing that all of your critical information is organized and accessible can help reduce the stress and anxiety that often accompany emergency situations. You can also save your loved ones from having to make difficult decisions during an already difficult time by having a clear plan in place for your end-of-life wishes.

I hope that this journal will be a useful resource for you and your life partner, assisting you in taking control of your affairs and feeling confident and prepared for whatever the future may hold. So, let's embark on this organizational and preparedness journey together!

QUICK START GUIDE

———

When a person dies without leaving a will, it means that they have died "intestate." This means that their property and assets will be distributed according to the laws of intestacy in their country or state. These laws vary from place to place, but typically, they provide a default distribution scheme that prioritizes certain family members over others.

For example, in many jurisdictions, if a person dies intestate and they are married with children, their spouse will inherit a portion of their assets, and the rest will be divided among their children. If the person had no children, their spouse might inherit everything. If the person was unmarried and had no children, their assets may go to their parents or siblings, depending on the laws of intestacy in their area.

The problem with dying intestate is that the distribution of assets may not reflect the wishes of the deceased. Additionally, it can be a complex and time-consuming process for loved ones to navigate, as they may need to go through a legal process to establish who is entitled to inherit the deceased's property. This can be particularly difficult in cases where there are disputes among family members or other interested parties.

Having a valid will in place can help to ensure that your assets are distributed according to your wishes after your death. It can also make things easier for your loved ones by providing clear instructions on what you want to happen with your property and assets.

Thank you for choosing the "Time to Get Our Affairs in Order" journal. This guide is designed to help you get started with the journal and provide tips for filling out each section.

Step 1:

Gather Your Information

Before you start filling out the journal, take some time to gather all the relevant information. This includes personal information such as your name, address, and date of birth, as well as financial, medical, and legal documents. You can also gather contact information for your family members, friends, and other important people in your life.

Step 2:

Read The Instructions

Each section of the journal has instructions on what information to include. Read these instructions carefully before filling out each section to ensure that you don't miss any important details.

Step 3:

Start Filling Out The Journal

Begin with Part I: Combined Information. This section is where you will combine your information as a couple or life partners. Here, you'll provide personal profiles, important contacts, financial information, real estate and property details, monthly bills and subscriptions, health and medical information, and final wishes and arrangements.

After Part I, you'll move on to Part II: Individual Information (Person A). This section is where Person A will fill out their personal information, important contacts, financial information, real estate and property details, monthly bills and subscriptions, health and medical information, legal documents, passwords and online accounts, thoughts and wishes, and a medications to-go page.

Then, you'll move on to Part III: Individual Information (Person B). This section is the same as Part II, but for Person B.

Step 4:

Use The Resources And To-Do List

At the end of the journal, you'll find a list of resources and organizations for replacing important documents, government resources, and support organizations.

You'll also find a to-do list that can help you keep track of the tasks that need to be completed to assist in completing the journal.

Step 5:
Keep Your Journal In A Secure Place

Once you've completed the journal, make sure to keep it in a secure place. You may want to make copies for your family members or trusted advisors, but be sure to keep the original in a safe and secure location.

I hope this Quick Start Guide has been helpful in getting you started with the "Time to Get Our Affairs in Order" journal. Remember, by taking the time to complete this journal, you are taking an important step in securing your future and protecting your loved ones.

PART 1:
EXPLANATION
(PERSON 1)

A s a husband and/or wife/ or partner, it's important to keep track of your person al information in one place and maybe even property/properties you both own. In this section, you'll combine your information in the following subsections:

In this section, Partner 1 will fill out the following ten subsections:

Personal Information

Personal information refers to any information that can be used to identify an individual. The name, address, phone number, email, social security number, date of birth, emergency contact information, employment history, and education history are all examples of personal information.

- **Name:** This is the name that a person goes by, which could include their first name, middle name, and last name. It's used to identify the individual.

- **Address:** This refers to the location where the individual resides or can be reached, such as a home or office address.

- **Phone number:** This is a set of digits used to contact the individual via phone call or text message.

- **Email:** This is an electronic address used to communicate with the individual online.

- **Social security number:** This is a unique nine-digit number issued by the government that identifies individuals for tax and social security purposes.

- **Date of birth:** This refers to the day, month, and year that an individual was born and is used to confirm their identity.

- **Emergency contact information:** This is the name, phone number, and relationship of a person to be contacted in case of an emergency.

- **Employment history:** This includes information about an individual's work experience, such as their job titles, employers, and dates of employment.

- **Education history:** This includes information about an individual's educational background, such as the name of schools attended, degrees earned, and graduation dates.

It's important to protect personal information as it can be used for identity theft, fraud, or other malicious purposes. Organizations that collect and store personal information have a responsibility to keep it safe and secure, and individuals should also take measures to protect their personal information, such as using strong passwords and being cautious about sharing it online.

Important Contacts

Important contacts refer to the individuals who should be notified or contacted in the event of an emergency, or those who are crucial to Person 1's daily life. These could include family members, friends, neighbors, or other individuals who have a close relationship with Person 1.

When listing important contacts, it's important to include the person's full name, phone number, email address, and their relationship to Person 1. This information can be used to quickly and easily contact these individuals in case of an emergency or if Person 1 needs assistance.

Family members are often the first individuals to be listed as important contacts, as they are typically the closest and most trusted people in one's life. This could include parents, siblings, children, or other relatives.

Friends and neighbors could also be important contacts, especially if Person 1 is not in contact with family members or lives far away from them. In case of an emergency or need for assistance, these individuals could help provide support or resources.

It's also important to consider any other individuals who play an important role in Person 1's life, such as a doctor, lawyer, or financial advisor. These individuals can provide important guidance and support in times of need.

Listing and regularly updating important contacts can be helpful in ensuring that Person 1 has a support system in place and that their loved ones are informed and able to help in case of an emergency.

Financial Information

Financial information refers to any information related to a person's financial situation, including their income, expenses, debts, assets, and investments. The financial information that may be important to include in a document could include:

- **Bank accounts:** This refers to any accounts held with financial institutions, such as checking accounts, savings accounts, or money market accounts.

- **Credit cards:** This refers to any credit cards that Person 1 may have, including the issuer, account number, and payment due dates.

- **Loans:** This refers to any outstanding loans that Person 1 may have, including mortgages, car loans, or personal loans. It's important to include the name of the lender, the amount owed, and the payment due date.

- **Investments:** This refers to any investments that Person 1 may have, such as stocks, bonds, mutual funds, or retirement accounts. It's important to include the name of the investment, the account number, and the institution where it's held.

- **Insurance policies:** This refers to any insurance policies that Person 1 may have, such as life insurance, health insurance, or auto insurance. It's important to include the name of the insurance company, the policy number, and the contact information for the agent or representative.

- **Taxes:** This refers to any information related to Person 1's tax situation, such as their tax ID number, past tax returns, and any outstanding tax debts.

- **Cryptocurrency and Bitcoin accounts:** This refers to any digital currency holdings, including Bitcoin and other cryptocurrencies. It's important to include the name of the cryptocurrency, the account number, and the platform where it's held.

Including this financial information in a document can be helpful for loved ones in the event of an emergency or if Person 1 is unable to manage their finances. It can also help with estate planning and ensuring that assets are distributed according to Person 1's wishes. However, it's important to keep this information secure and to only share it with trusted individuals.

Real Estate and Property

Real estate and property refer to any physical assets that Person 1 owns, including their home, rental properties, vehicles, land, and any other assets of value. When documenting real estate and property, it's important to include the following details:

- **Value:** This refers to the estimated value of the property or asset. This can be determined through appraisals or market research.

- **Location:** This refers to the physical address of the property or asset.

- **Ownership details:** This refers to the legal ownership of the property or asset, including any liens or mortgages that may be attached to it.

For homes and rental properties, it's important to include the name of the mortgage lender, the loan number, and the contact information for the lender. For vehicles, it's important to include the make, model, and year of the vehicle, as well as the vehicle identification number (VIN).

In the case of land, it's important to include the location of the land, the legal description of the property, and any survey information. It may also be helpful to include any zoning or land use restrictions that may apply to the property.

By documenting real estate and property, Person 1 can ensure that their loved ones are aware of their assets and that they are distributed according to their wishes in the event of their death or incapacity. It can also help with estate planning and tax planning. However, it's important to keep this information secure and to only share it with trusted individuals.

Monthly Bills and Subscriptions

Monthly bills and subscriptions refer to any recurring expenses that Person 1 may have, including bills for utilities, rent/mortgage payments, subscriptions for magazines, streaming services, gym memberships, and any other monthly payments.

When documenting monthly bills and subscriptions, it's important to include the following details:

- **Due dates:** This refers to the date on which the bill or subscription payment is due.

- **Amounts:** This refers to the cost of the bill or subscription.

- **Payment methods:** This refers to the method that Person 1 uses to pay the bill or subscription, such as automatic bank transfers or credit card payments.

Having a record of monthly bills and subscriptions can be helpful for both Person 1 and their loved ones. It can help Person 1 keep track of their expenses and ensure that bills are paid on time. In the event that Person 1 is unable to manage their finances, having a record of their bills and subscriptions can help loved ones ensure that these payments are still being made on time.

It's also important to regularly review and update this information, as monthly bills and subscriptions can change over time. By keeping this information up to date, Person 1 can ensure that their loved ones have access to the most current information in case of an emergency.

Health and Medical Information

Health and medical information refers to any information related to Person 1's medical history, current medical conditions, allergies, medications, and doctors they may be seeing. When documenting health and medical information, it's important to include the following details:

- **Medical history:** This refers to any previous medical conditions or surgeries that Person 1 has had.

- **Current medical conditions:** This refers to any ongoing medical conditions that Person 1 is currently managing.

- **Allergies:** This refers to any allergies that Person 1 may have to medications, food, or other substances.

- **Medications:** This refers to any medications that Person 1 is currently taking, including dosage and frequency.

- **Doctors:** This refers to any doctors or healthcare providers that Person 1 is seeing, including their names, specialties, and contact information.

Having a record of health and medical information can be critical in the event of an emergency. It can help medical professionals make informed decisions about Person 1's care, especially if they are unable to communicate or if their loved ones are not present to provide this information. It can also be helpful for personal health management, ensuring that Person 1 is aware of their own medical history and any ongoing conditions they may be managing.

However, it's important to keep this information private and secure, and to only share it with trusted individuals such as healthcare providers or designated emergency contacts.

Legal Documents

Legal documents refer to any documents that have legal significance, such as a will, power of attorney, living will, prenuptial agreement, cohabitation agreement, or any other legal documents that Person 1 may have. When documenting legal documents, it's important to include the following details:

- **Location:** This refers to where the original documents are stored, such as a safe deposit box, lawyer's office, or home safe.

- **Contact information:** This refers to the contact information for any lawyers or legal professionals involved in drafting or executing the documents, as well as any individuals named in the documents, such as an executor or power of attorney.

Having a record of legal documents can be critical in ensuring that Person 1's wishes are carried out in the event of their death or incapacity. It can also be helpful for personal legal management, ensuring that Person 1 is aware of their legal rights and obligations. It's important to keep these documents private and secure, and to only share them with trusted individuals such as lawyers or designated emergency contacts. Additionally, it's important to regularly review and update these documents as circumstances may change over time, such as changes in family relationships, health status, or financial situations.

Passwords and Online Accounts

Passwords and online accounts refer to any usernames and passwords that Person 1 may use for online accounts, websites, and other digital services, as well as any passwords for electronic devices, safes, or safety deposit boxes. When documenting passwords and online accounts, it's important to include the following details:

- **Username:** This refers to the username or account name associated with the online account or digital service.

- **Password:** This refers to the password associated with the username or account name.

- **Website or service:** This refers to the website or digital service associated with the username and password.

Having a record of passwords and online accounts can be helpful for both personal use and emergency situations. It can help Person 1 keep track of their accounts and ensure that they are able to access them when needed. In the event that Person 1 is unable to manage their accounts, having a record of their passwords and accounts can help loved ones access important information or accounts on their behalf.

However, it's important to keep this information private and secure, and to only share it with trusted individuals such as designated emergency contacts. It's also important to regularly update passwords and review account activity to ensure that they remain secure and protected against any potential security breaches.

Thoughts and Wishes

Thoughts and wishes refer to any personal reflections, aspirations, or goals that Person 1 may have for their future. When documenting thoughts and wishes, it's important to include the following details:

- **Personal thoughts:** This refers to any personal reflections or musings that Person 1 may have, such as memories, experiences, or personal philosophies.

- **Inspirations:** This refers to any sources of inspiration that Person 1 may have, such as books, music, or art.

- **Wishes for the future:** This refers to any aspirations or goals that Person 1 may have for their future, such as travel plans, career goals, or personal milestones.

Having a record of thoughts and wishes can be helpful for personal reflection and goal-setting, as well as for loved ones who may want to understand Person 1's perspectives or values. It can also provide comfort in the event of Person 1's passing, as loved ones may be able to honor their wishes or reflect on their personal thoughts.

However, it's important to ensure that thoughts and wishes are kept private and secure, and that they are only shared with trusted individuals or designated emergency contacts. Additionally, it's important to regularly review and update thoughts and wishes as circumstances or goals may change over time.

Medications To-Go Page

The Medications To-Go page is a document that contains a list of Person 1's medications and dosages, which can be used in emergency situations. When documenting medications to-go, it's important to include the following details:

- **Medication name:** This refers to the name of the medication that Person 1 is taking.

- **Dosage:** This refers to the amount of medication that Person 1 is taking, as well as how often it should be taken.

- **Route of administration:** This refers to how the medication should be taken, such as orally, through injection, or topically.

Having a list of medications and dosages can be critical in emergency situations, especially if Person 1 is unable to communicate their medical history or current medications. The Medications To-Go page can be kept in a convenient location such as a wallet or purse, and can be used to quickly provide information to emergency responders or medical professionals.

However, it's important to ensure that the Medications To-Go page is regularly updated and that any changes to medications or dosages are reflected on the document. It's also important to consult with a healthcare provider before making any changes to medication regimens or dosages.

PART 1:
INDIVIDUAL INFORMATION (Person 1)

Individual Information refers to the personal details and background information about Person 1. This information can be important for both personal reference and emergency situations. When documenting Individual Information, it's important to include the following details:

- **Full name:** This refers to the legal name of Person 1.

- **Address:** This refers to the current physical address of Person 1, as well as any other relevant addresses (such as previous addresses or vacation homes).

- **Phone number:** This refers to the primary phone number where Person 1 can be reached.

- **Email address:** This refers to the primary email address where Person 1 can be reached.

- **Social Security number:** This refers to Person 1's unique nine-digit Social Security number, which is used for tax and other government-related purposes.

- **Date of birth:** This refers to Person 1's date of birth.

- **Emergency contact information:** This refers to the name, phone number, and relationship of the person who should be contacted in case of an emergency.

- **Employment history:** This refers to Person 1's previous and current employment, including job titles, employers, and dates of employment.

- **Education history:** This refers to Person 1's educational background, including degrees, institutions attended, and dates of attendance.

Having a record of Individual Information can be helpful for personal reference and in emergency situations where this information may be needed quickly. However, it's important to ensure that this information is kept private and secure, and that it is only shared with trusted individuals or designated emergency contacts. Additionally, it's important to regularly review and update Individual Information as circumstances may change over time.

Husband/Wife/Life Partner 1:

Personal information for Husband/Wife/Life Partner 1 refers to the personal details and background information about the person's spouse or partner. When documenting Personal Information for Husband/Wife/Life Partner 1, it's important to include the following details.

- **Full name**: This refers to the legal name of the person's spouse or partner.

- **Date of birth:** This refers to the date of birth of the person's spouse or partner.

- **Contact information:** This includes the phone number, email address, and physical address of the person's spouse or partner.

- **Social Security number:** This refers to the unique nine-digit Social Security number of the person's spouse or partner, which is used for tax and other government-related purposes.

- **Employment history:** This includes the previous and current employment history of the person's spouse or partner, including job titles, employers, and dates of employment.

- **Education history:** This includes the educational background of the person's spouse or partner, including degrees, institutions attended, and dates of attendance.

Having a record of Personal Information for Husband/Wife/Life Partner 1 can be helpful for personal reference and in emergency situations where this information may be needed quickly. However, it's important to ensure that this information is kept private and secure, and that it is only shared with trusted individuals or designated emergency contacts. Additionally, it's important to regularly review and update this information as circumstances may change over time.

Personal Information:

Full Name: _____

Address: _____

City: _____

State: _____ Zip Code: _____

Country: _____

Home: _____

Mobile: _____

Work: _____

Home eMail: _____

Date of Birth: _____

Social Security Number: _____

In this section, the first partner will fill out the following ten subsections:

Emergency Contact Information:

Emergency Contact Information refers to the names, phone numbers, and relationships of the people who should be contacted in case of an emergency. When documenting Emergency Contact Information, it's important to include the following details:

- **Name:** This refers to the full name of the emergency contact.

- **Phone number:** This refers to the primary phone number where the emergency contact can be reached.

- **Email address:** This refers to the primary email address where the emergency contact can be reached.

- **Relationship:** This refers to the relationship of the emergency contact to the person who is creating the document. Examples of relationships can include spouse, child, parent, sibling, friend, neighbor, or colleague.

Having a record of Emergency Contact Information can be extremely helpful in case of an emergency, such as a sudden illness, injury, or accident. By having this information readily available, emergency responders and medical professionals can quickly contact the appropriate people and provide important updates about the person's condition. It's important to keep this information up-to-date and to inform the emergency contacts that they have been designated as such.

Person 1

Full Name: _____

Address: _____

City: _____

State: _____ Zip Code: _____

Country: _____

Home: _____

Mobile: _____

Work: _____

Home eMail: _____

Date of Birth: _____

Social Security Number: _____

Phone: _____

eMail: _____

Relationship: _____

Other Important Details: _____

_____

_____

Emergency Contact Information (Person 2)

Emergency Contact Information for Person 2 refers to the names, phone numbers, and relationships of the people who should be contacted in case of an emergency for Person 2. When documenting Emergency Contact Information for Person 2, it's important to include the following details:

- **Name:** This refers to the full name of the emergency contact for Person 2.

- **Phone number:** This refers to the primary phone number where the emergency contact can be reached in case of an emergency related to

Person 2.

- **Email address:** This refers to the primary email address where the emergency contact can be reached in case of an emergency related to Person 2.

- **Relationship:** This refers to the relationship of the emergency contact to Person 2. Examples of relationships can include spouse, child, parent, sibling, friend, neighbor, or colleague.

In some cases, it may also be useful to include additional information about the emergency contact, such as their address, workplace, or any other relevant details that may be needed in an emergency situation.

Having Emergency Contact Information for Person 2 can be crucial in case of an emergency, such as a sudden illness, injury, or accident that renders Person 2 unable to communicate or make decisions. By having this information readily available, emergency responders and medical professionals can quickly contact the appropriate people and provide important updates about Person 2's condition. It's important to keep this information up-to-date and to inform the emergency contacts that they have been designated as such.

Person 2

Full Name: _____

Address: _____

City: _____

State: _____ Zip Code: _____

Country: _____

Home: _____

Mobile: _____

Work: _____

Home eMail: _____

Date of Birth: _____

Social Security Number: _____

Phone: _____

eMail: _____

Relationship: _____

Other Important Details: _____

_____

Employment

Employment information for Person 1 refers to the details of their current or previous employment. When documenting Employment Information for Person 1, it's important to include the following details:

- **Employer name:** This refers to the name of Person 1's current or previous employer.

- **Job title:** This refers to the job title of Person 1's current or previous role.

- **Start and end date:** This refers to the start and end date of Person 1's employment in that role.

- **Salary:** This refers to the salary or hourly wage that Person 1 received for their work.

- **Contact information:** This refers to the contact information of the employer, including the address, phone number, and email address.

Additionally, it may also be useful to include information about any benefits or retirement plans that Person 1 is enrolled in, as well as any relevant human resources contact information.

Having accurate Employment Information for Person 1 can be important for a number of reasons, such as when applying for loans or other financial services, or for tax purposes. It can also be helpful to have this information readily available in case of an emergency, such as if Person 1 is suddenly unable to work due to illness or injury.

Employer Name: _____

Job Title: _____

Work Address: _____

Work Phone: _____

Date of Hire: _____ Annual Salary: _____

Education History

Education history refers to the academic and educational background of a person, which includes information on their degrees, diplomas, and certifications. When documenting Education History, it is important to include the following details:

- **Institution Name:** This refers to the name of the educational institution where the person studied.

- **Degree/Certificate:** This refers to the type of degree or certificate that the person earned, such as a Bachelor's degree, Master's degree, or a professional certification.

- **Major/Area of Study:** This refers to the subject or field that the person specialized in while pursuing their degree or certificate.

- **Dates Attended:** This refers to the duration of time that the person was enrolled in the educational institution.

- **Honors/ Awards:** This refers to any honors or awards received by the person during their academic journey, such as a summa cum laude or magna cum laude distinction.

It may also be useful to include any additional information such as the location of the educational institution, the name of the program or department, and the contact information of the school's registrar office.

Having accurate Education History information for a person is important in a number of scenarios, such as job applications, further education pursuits, or even for personal records. It can also be helpful to have this information readily available in case of an emergency, such as if a person requires medical treatment and the healthcare provider needs to know their educational background.

Highest Degree Earned: _____

Institution Name: _____

Field of Study: _____

Degree Type: _____ Graduation Date: _____

Family Information

Family information refers to the details of the family members of a person, such as their spouse, children, parents, and siblings. When documenting Family Information, it is important to include the following details:

- **Name:** This refers to the name of each family member, including their first and last name.

- **Relationship:** This refers to the relationship of the family member to the person, such as spouse, parent, child, or sibliwng.

- **Date of Birth:** This refers to the date of birth of each family member.

- **Contact Information:** This refers to the contact information of each family member, including their phone number, email address, and physical address.

Additionally, it may also be useful to include information about any important events related to family members, such as weddings, births, or deaths.

Having accurate Family Information for a person can be important for a number of reasons, such as when planning family events or reunions, or for medical reasons such as in case of genetic disorders or family medical history. It can also be helpful to have this information readily available in case of an emergency, such as if a family member needs to be contacted quickly.

The subsections for this section can include:

Details for family members

Spouse

A spouse refers to a person's husband or wife, in a legally recognized marriage. When documenting information about a spouse, it is important to include the following details:

- **Personal Information:** This includes the spouse's full name, date of birth, place of birth, and contact information such as phone number, email address, and physical address.

- **Marriage Information:** This includes the date and location of the marriage, as well as any other details relevant to the marriage, such as whether it was a civil or religious ceremony.

- **Employment Information:** This includes the spouse's employment history, including their current employer, job title, and length of employment.

- **Education Information:** This includes the spouse's education history, including the schools they attended, degrees earned, and areas of study.

- **Family Information:** This includes details about the spouse's family members, such as their parents and siblings, including their names, dates of birth, and contact information.

Having accurate information about a spouse is important for a number of reasons, such as for legal and financial matters, healthcare decisions, and emergency situations. It is also important to keep this information up to date in case of any changes, such as a change of address or employment.

PART 1: INDIVIDUAL INFORMATION (Person 1)

Full Name: _____

Address: _____

City: _____

State: _____ Zip Code: _____

Country: _____

Home: _____

Mobile: _____

Work: _____

Home eMail: _____

Date of Birth: _____

Social Security Number: _____

Spouse's Employment

When documenting a spouse's employment information, it is important to include details such as:

- **Current Employer:** This includes the name of the spouse's current employer.

- **Job Title:** This refers to the title or position held by the spouse in their current job.

- **Date of Employment:** This refers to the date the spouse started working with their current employer.

- **Work Contact Information:** This includes the phone number, email address, and physical address of the spouse's workplace.

- **Work History:** This includes the spouse's work history, such as previous employers, job titles, and dates of employment.

Having accurate employment information for a spouse can be important for a number of reasons, such as for tax purposes, loan applications, or in the event of an emergency. It can also be useful to keep this information up to date in case of any changes, such as a change in job or employer.

Employer Name: _____

Job Title: _____

Work Address: _____

Work Phone: _____

Date of Hire: _____ Annual Salary: _____

Spouse's Education History

When documenting a spouse's education history, it is important to include details such as:

- **Schools Attended:** This includes the names of the schools the spouse attended, including the name of the institution and the name of the degree program.

- **Degree(s) Earned:** This includes the type of degree(s) the spouse earned, such as a Bachelor's, Master's, or Doctorate degree.

- **Area(s) of Study:** This includes the subject area or field of study the spouse pursued, such as business, engineering, or education.

- **Dates of Attendance:** This includes the dates when the spouse attended each school, including the start and end dates.

Having accurate education information for a spouse can be important for a number of reasons, such as for job applications, educational opportunities, or in the event of an emergency. It can also be useful to keep this information up to date in case of any changes, such as completing a new degree program or pursuing further education.

Highest Degree Earned: _____

Institution Name: _____

Field of Study: _____

Degree Type: _____ Graduation Date: _____

Children

When documenting information about children, it is important to include details such as:

- **Full Name:** This includes the full name of each child.

- **Date of Birth:** This refers to the date of birth of each child.

- **Relationship:** This indicates the relationship of each child to the person or couple documenting the information, such as "biological child," "adopted child," "stepchild," etc.

- **Contact Information:** This includes the phone number, email address, and physical address of each child.

- **School Information:** This includes the name and address of the school each child attends, as well as their grade level.

- **Medical Information:** This includes any relevant medical information about each child, such as allergies or chronic conditions.

Having accurate information about children can be important for a number of reasons, such as for medical emergencies, school activities, or in the event of a legal dispute. It can also be useful to keep this information up to date in case of any changes, such as a change in school or medical condition.

• First Child

Full Name: _____

Address: _____

City: _____

State: _____ Zip Code: _____

Country: _____

Phone: _____

eMail: _____

Date of Birth: _____

Social Security Number: _____

Education: _____

• Second Child

Full Name: _____

Address: _____

City: _____

State: _____ Zip Code: _____

Country: _____

Phone: _____

eMail: _____

Date of Birth: _____

Social Security Number: _____

Education: _____

• Third Child

Full Name: _____

Address: _____

City: _____

State: _____ Zip Code: _____

Country: _____

Phone: _____

eMail: _____

Date of Birth: _____

Social Security Number: _____

Education: _____

• Fourth Child

Full Name: _____

Address: _____

City: _____

State: _____ Zip Code: _____

Country: _____

Phone: _____

eMail: _____

Date of Birth: _____

Social Security Number: _____

Education: _____

Parents

When documenting information about parents, it is important to include details such as:

- **Full Name:** This includes the full name of each parent.

- **Date of Birth:** This refers to the date of birth of each parent.

- **Contact Information:** This includes the phone number, email address, and physical address of each parent.

- **Medical Information:** This includes any relevant medical information about each parent, such as allergies or chronic conditions.

- **Employment Information:** This includes information about each parent's employment, such as their job title, company name, and contact information.

- **Education History:** This includes information about each parent's education history, such as the schools they attended and the degrees they earned.

Having accurate information about parents can be important for a number of reasons, such as for medical emergencies, family history research, or in the event of a legal dispute. It can also be useful to keep this information up to date in case of any changes, such as a change in contact information or medical condition.

• Father

Full Name: _____

Address: _____

City: _____

State: _____ Zip Code: _____

Country: _____

Phone: _____

eMail: _____

Date of Birth: _____

Social Security Number: _____

Education: _____

Other Important Details: _____

• Mother

Full Name: _____

Address: _____

City: _____

State: _____ Zip Code: _____

Country: _____

Phone: _____

eMail: _____

Date of Birth: _____

Social Security Number: _____

Education: _____

Other Important Details: _____

• Siblings

Full Name: _____

Address: _____

City: _____

State: _____ Zip Code: _____

Country: _____

Phone: _____

eMail: _____

Date of Birth: _____

Social Security Number: _____

Education: _____

Other Important Details: _____

• Siblings

Full Name: _____

Address: _____

City: _____

State: _____ Zip Code: _____

Country: _____

Phone: _____

eMail: _____

Date of Birth: _____

Social Security Number: _____

Education: _____

Other Important Details: _____

• Siblings

Full Name: _____

Address: _____

City: _____

State: _____ Zip Code: _____

Country: _____

Phone: _____

eMail: _____

Date of Birth: _____

Social Security Number: _____

Education: _____

Other Important Details: _____

Other Family Members:

When documenting information about other family members, it is important to include details such as:

PART 1: INDIVIDUAL INFORMATION (Person 1)

- **Full Name:** This includes the full name of each family member.

- **Date of Birth:** This refers to the date of birth of each family member.

- **Relationship:** This indicates the relationship of each family member to the person or couple documenting the information, such as "sibling," "grandparent," "cousin," etc.

- **Contact Information:** This includes the phone number, email address, and physical address of each family member.

- **Medical Information:** This includes any relevant medical information about each family member, such as allergies or chronic conditions.

- **Employment Information:** This includes information about each family member's employment, such as their job title, company name, and contact information.

- **Education History:** This includes information about each family member's education history, such as the schools they attended and the degrees they earned.

Having accurate information about other family members can be important for a number of reasons, such as for medical emergencies, family history research, or in the event of a legal dispute. It can also be useful to keep this information up to date in case of any changes, such as a change in contact information or medical condition.

Full Name: _____

Address: _____

City: _____

State: _____ Zip Code: _____

Country: _____

Phone: _____

eMail: _____

Relationship: _____

Other Important Details: _____

_____

_____

Full Name: _____

Address: _____

City: _____

State: _____ Zip Code: _____

Country: _____

Phone: _____

eMail: _____

Relationship: _____

Other Important Details: _____

_____

_____

Chapter 1:

FINANCIAL INFORMATION

———

Financial information is an important part of any personal information document. Here are some details that can be included under this section:

- **Bank Accounts:** This includes details of all bank accounts held by the person, including the name of the bank, account number, account type (savings or checking), and the current balance.

- **Credit Cards:** This includes a list of all credit cards held by the person, including the name of the card issuer, card number, and the current balance.

- **Loans:** This includes details of any loans taken out by the person, including the name of the lender, the loan amount, and the current balance.

- **Investments:** This includes details of any investments made by the person, including the name of the investment, the amount invested, and the current value.

- **Insurance Policies:** This includes details of all insurance policies held by the person, including life insurance, health insurance, car insurance, and home insurance.

- **Taxes:** This includes details of the person's tax status, including their tax ID number, filing status, and any outstanding tax payments.

- **Cryptocurrency:** This includes information about any cryptocurrency owned by the person, such as Bitcoin or Ethereum, including the amount owned and any associated wallets or accounts.

It is important to keep this financial information up to date, as changes in bank accounts, credit cards, loans, and investments can happen frequently. This information can be used to help manage the person's finances in case of incapacity or to help their executor handle their finances after they pass away.

Bank Information

Bank information is an important part of the financial information section in a personal information document. Here are some details that can be included under this section:

- **Name of the bank:** This includes the name of the bank where the person holds their account.

- **Account number:** This includes the account number of the person's bank account(s).

- **Account type:** This includes information about the type of account, such as savings, checking, or money market.

- **Current balance:** This includes the current balance of the account(s).

It is important to keep this information up to date and accurate, as it can be used to manage the person's finances in case of incapacity or to help their executor handle their finances after they pass away. It is also important to keep this information secure and confidential, as it contains sensitive financial information. A personal information document should be stored in a safe and secure location, such as a locked safe or a secure digital file with proper encryption.

Bank Name: _____

Account Type: _____

Account Number: _____

Routing Number: _____

Online Login URL: _____

Online Login Username: _____

Online Login Password: _____

Credit Cards

Credit card information is another important aspect of the financial information section in a personal information document. Here are some details that can be included under this section:

- **Credit card issuer:** This includes the name of the credit card issuer, such as Visa, Mastercard, or American Express.

- **Credit card number:** This includes the 16-digit credit card number.

- **Expiration date:** This includes the month and year that the credit card expires.

- **Security code:** This includes the three-digit security code on the back of the credit card.

- **Credit limit:** This includes the maximum amount that can be charged to the credit card.

It is important to keep this information up to date and accurate, as it can be used to manage the person's finances in case of incapacity or to help their executor handle their finances after they pass away. It is also important to keep this information secure and confidential, as it contains sensitive financial information. A personal information document should be stored in a safe and secure location, such as a locked safe or a secure digital file with proper encryption.

Card Issuer: _____

Card Type: _____

Card Number: _____

Expiration Date: _____

Security Code: _____

Balance: _____

Online Login URL: _____

Online Login Username: _____

Online Login Password: _____

Loans

Another aspect of financial information is loans. This can include:

- **Loan issuer:** This includes the name of the institution or organization that issued the loan.

- **Loan type:** This includes the type of loan, such as a mortgage, personal loan, or student loan.

- **Loan balance:** This includes the outstanding balance on the loan.

- **Interest rate:** This includes the interest rate on the loan.

- **Payment schedule:** This includes the frequency and amount of loan payments.

- **Collateral:** This includes any collateral put up for the loan, such as a house or a car.

Keeping track of loan information is important for financial planning and management. It can also be helpful for an executor in settling the person's estate after they pass away. Like with credit card information, it's important to keep loan information secure and confidential. A personal information document should be stored in a safe and secure location, such as a locked safe or a secure digital file with proper encryption.

Lender Name: _____

Lender Type: _____

Loan Amount: _____

Interest Rate: _____

Monthly Payment: _____

Due Date: _____

Remaining Balance: _____

Online Login URL: _____

Online Login Username: _____

Online Login Password: _____

Loans Continued

In addition to the primary loan information that was mentioned earlier, here are a few more details to consider adding:

- **Payment history:** This includes a record of past payments made on the loan.

- **Loan purpose:** This includes why the loan was taken out, such as for a car, education, or home improvement.

- **Loan terms:** This includes the length of the loan and any other terms and conditions associated with it.

- **Co-signers:** If someone else co-signed the loan, it's important to include their name and contact information.

Having a complete record of loans is important not just for financial planning and management, but also in case of unexpected events such as disability or death. In such cases, the executor of the estate may need to contact the loan issuer to make arrangements for payment or transfer of the loan.

Lender Name: _____

Lender Type: _____

Loan Amount: _____

Interest Rate: _____

Monthly Payment:
Lender Name: _____

Lender Type: _____

Loan Amount: _____

Interest Rate: _____

Monthly Payment: _____

Due Date: _____

Remaining Balance: _____

Online Login URL: _____

Online Login Username: _____

Online Login Password: _____

Lender Name: _____

Lender Type: _____

Loan Amount: _____

Interest Rate: _____

Monthly Payment: _____

Due Date: _____

Remaining Balance: _____

Online Login URL: _____

Online Login Username: _____

Online Login Password: _____

Loans Continued

In addition to the basic loan information that was mentioned earlier, here are a few more details to consider adding:

- **Payment history:** This includes a record of past payments made on the loan.

- **Loan purpose:** This includes why the loan was taken out, such as for a car, education, or home improvement.

- **Loan terms:** This includes the length of the loan and any other terms and conditions associated with it.

- **Co-signers:** If someone else co-signed the loan, it's important to include their name and contact information.

Having a complete record of loans is important not just for financial planning and management, but also in case of unexpected events such as disability or death. In such cases, the executor of the estate may need to contact the loan issuer to make arrangements for payment or transfer of the loan.

Lender Name: _____

Lender Type: _____

Loan Amount: _____

Interest Rate: _____

Monthly Payment: _____

Due Date: _____

Remaining Balance: _____

Online Login URL: _____

Online Login Username: _____

Online Login Password: _____

Investments

When it comes to financial planning, investments can play an important role in building wealth and achieving long-term financial goals. Here are some pieces of information to consider including in your investment section:

- **Investment accounts:** This includes the names and account numbers of any investment accounts, such as brokerage accounts or retirement accounts.

- **Investment holdings:** This includes the specific investments held within each account, such as stocks, bonds, mutual funds, or exchange-traded funds (ETFs).

- **Investment value:** This includes the current value of each investment account and the estimated value of each holding.

- **Investment advisors:** If you work with a financial advisor, it's important to include their name, contact information, and any relevant account numbers or other details.

- **Investment goals:** It can be helpful to include your long-term investment goals, such as retirement or saving for a child's education.

By keeping a comprehensive record of your investment accounts and holdings, you can stay on top of your investment strategy and make informed decisions about your financial future. Additionally, having this information readily available can be helpful for your loved ones in case of incapacity or death.

Investment Firm: _____

Account Type: _____

Account Number: _____

Investment Type: _____

Investment Value: _____

Current Yield: _____

Date of Last Transaction: _____

Balance: _____

Online Login URL: _____

Online Login Username: _____

Online Login Password: _____

Investment Firm: _____

Account Type: _____

Account Number: _____

Investment Type: _____

Investment Value: _____

Current Yield: _____

Date of Last Transaction: _____

Balance: _____

Online Login URL: _____

Online Login Username: _____

Online Login Password: _____

Investments Continued

Here are some additional pieces of information to consider including in the investments section:

- **Investment income:** This includes any income generated by your investments, such as dividends, interest, or capital gains.

- **Investment expenses:** This includes any fees or expenses associated with your investments, such as management fees or trading fees.

- **Investment performance:** This includes the historical performance of your investments, such as annual returns or growth rates.

- **Investment strategy:** This includes your overall investment strategy and approach, such as your risk tolerance, asset allocation, and diversification strategy.

- **Investment documents:** This includes any important investment-related documents, such as account statements, trade confirmations, and tax documents.

By including this information in your investment section, you can have a more comprehensive view of your investment portfolio and strategy. This can be especially helpful when reviewing your investments with a financial advisor or when making investment decisions on your own. Additionally, having this information organized and easily accessible can be helpful for your loved ones in the event of incapacity or death.

Investment Firm: _____

Account Type: _____

Account Number: _____

Investment Type: _____

Investment Value: _____

Current Yield: _____

Date of Last Transaction: _____

Balance: _____

Online Login URL: _____

Online Login Username: _____

Online Login Password: _____

Investment Firm: _____

Account Type: _____

Account Number: _____

Investment Type: _____

Investment Value: _____

Current Yield: _____

Date of Last Transaction: _____

Balance: _____

Online Login URL: _____

Online Login Username: _____

Online Login Password: _____

Insurance Agency

The insurance agency section of a personal information organizer typically includes information about the insurance policies that a person has. This can include details about health insurance, life insurance, car insurance, home insurance, and any other insurance policies that the person holds.

Here are some pieces of information that you may want to include in the insurance agency section:

- **Insurance policy type:** This includes the type of insurance policy that you have, such as health insurance, life insurance, auto insurance, or homeowner's insurance.

- **Insurance provider name:** This includes the name of the insurance company that provides your policy.

- **Policy number:** This is the unique identification number associated with your policy.

- **Policy start and end date:** This includes the dates that your policy started and will end.

- **Policy coverage and limits:** This includes the types of coverage included in your policy and the limits of coverage for each type.

- **Premium amount:** This is the amount of money that you pay for your insurance policy, typically on a monthly or annual basis.

- **Payment information:** This includes information about how you pay your insurance premiums, such as the payment method and due date.

- **Agent contact information:** This includes the name, phone number, and email address of your insurance agent.

By organizing all of your insurance policy information in one place, you can easily keep track of your coverage, premiums, and important contact information. This can be especially helpful in the event of an emergency, where quick access to insurance information may be necessary.

Insurance Company: _____

Policy Type: _____

Policy Number: _____

Coverage: _____

Beneficiary: _____

Online Login URL: _____

Online Login Username: _____

Online Login Password: _____

Insurance Company: _____

Policy Type: _____

Policy Number: _____

Coverage: _____

Beneficiary: _____

Online Login URL: _____

Online Login Username: _____

Online Login Password: _____

Insurance Continued

In the context of the personal finance and estate planning, insurance refers to the various policies a person may hold to protect themselves and their loved ones in the event of unexpected events or accidents. Some common types of insurance include:

- **Life insurance:** provides a payout to designated beneficiaries upon the policyholder's death.

- **Health insurance:** helps cover the costs of medical care and treatment.

- **Homeowner's insurance:** protects the policyholder's home and property in the event of damage or theft.

- **Auto insurance:** covers the policyholder's vehicle in the event of damage or accidents.

- **Disability insurance:** provides income replacement in the event of an illness or injury that prevents the policyholder from working.

- **Long-term care insurance:** covers the costs of long-term care, such as assisted living or nursing home care.

When organizing financial information for estate planning purposes, it is important to include details about insurance policies, such as the policy number, the name of the insurance company, and the contact information for the agent or representative who handles the policy. This information can help ensure that beneficiaries are able to access the benefits they are entitled to in a timely and efficient manner.

Insurance Company: _____

Policy Type: _____

Policy Number: _____

Coverage: _____

Beneficiary: _____

Online Login URL: _____

Online Login Username: _____

Online Login Password: _____

Insurance Company: _____

Policy Type: _____

Policy Number: _____

Coverage: _____

Beneficiary: _____

Online Login URL: _____

Online Login Username: _____

Online Login Password: _____

Insurance Company: _____

Policy Type: _____

Policy Number: _____

Coverage: _____

Beneficiary: _____

Online Login URL: _____

Online Login Username: _____

Online Login Password: _____

Taxes

Taxes are a crucial aspect of personal finance and estate planning. In general, taxes are payments made to the government to support public services and infrastructure, and they are usually assessed based on income, property, and other financial activities. Here are some important aspects of taxes to consider when organizing financial information for estate planning purposes:

- **Income taxes:** Individuals are required to pay taxes on the income they earn from various sources, including wages, salaries, investments, and rental income. Income taxes can vary depending on the amount of income earned and the tax bracket the individual falls into.

- **Property taxes:** Property taxes are assessed on real estate and other property owned by the individual. The amount of property tax owed is usually based on the assessed value of the property.

- **Estate taxes:** When an individual passes away, their estate may be subject to estate taxes, which are taxes assessed on the value of the assets that make up the estate. The threshold for estate taxes varies by state and country.

When organizing financial information for estate planning purposes, it is important to include details about the taxes that the individual is currently paying or may be responsible for in the future. This can include information such as the current tax rate, the amount of taxes owed, and the due date for filing tax returns. Additionally, it is important to consider any tax implications of estate planning decisions, such as how a particular asset may be taxed when it is transferred to a beneficiary.

Tax Year: _____

Filing Status: _____

Filing Deadline: _____

Taxable Income: _____

Deductions: _____

Credits: _____

Tax Owed/Refund: _____

Online Tax Account URL: _____

Online Tax Account Username: _____

Online Tax Account Password: _____

Tax Year: _____

Filing Status: _____

Filing Deadline: _____

Taxable Income: _____

Deductions: _____

Credits: _____

Tax Owed/Refund: _____

Online Tax Account URL: _____

Online Tax Account Username: _____

Online Tax Account Password: _____

Taxes Continued

In the context of personal finances, taxes refer to the money that an individual is required to pay to the government based on their income and other factors. The information related to taxes in a personal information document can include details about the types of taxes that Person 1 owes, such as income tax, property tax, or capital gains tax. It can also include information about any tax deductions, credits, or exemptions that Person 1 is eligible for.

In addition to this, the document can also include information about any past tax returns that Person 1 has filed, along with the contact information for their tax accountant or tax attorney. This information can be useful in the event of an audit or any other tax-related issues that may arise in the future.

Tax Year: _____

Filing Status: _____

Filing Deadline: _____

Taxable Income: _____

Deductions: _____

Credits: _____

Tax Owed/Refund: _____

Online Tax Account URL: _____

Online Tax Account Username: _____

Online Tax Account Password: _____

Tax Year: _____

Filing Status: _____

Filing Deadline: _____

Taxable Income: _____

Deductions: _____

Credits: _____

Tax Owed/Refund: _____

Online Tax Account URL: _____

Online Tax Account Username: _____

Online Tax Account Password: _____

Cryptocurrency / Bitcoin Accounts

Cryptocurrency and Bitcoin accounts are digital assets that can hold and transfer value, typically without the need for a central authority or intermediary. In the context of a personal information document, information related to cryptocurrency and Bitcoin accounts can include details about the types of cryptocurrencies that Person 1 owns, the amount of each cryptocurrency, and the location of the wallets or exchanges where the cryptocurrencies are held.

This information can be important for a number of reasons, such as facilitating the transfer of cryptocurrency assets to heirs or beneficiaries in the event of Person 1's death. It can also help to ensure that Person 1's cryptocurrency assets are protected and secure, by providing information about any passwords, private keys, or other security measures that are in place to protect the accounts.

Cryptocurrency or Bitcoin Exchange: _____

Wallet address: _____

Currency Type (e.g. Bitcoin, Ethereum, Solana, Tron etc.): _____

Balance: _____

Private Key: _____

Public Key: _____

Online Login URL: _____

Online Login Username: _____

Online Login Password: _____

Cryptocurrency or Bitcoin Exchange: _____

Wallet address: _____

Currency Type (e.g. Bitcoin, Ethereum, Solana, Tron etc.): _____

Balance: _____

Private Key: _____

Public Key: _____

Online Login URL: _____

Online Login Username: _____

Online Login Password: _____

Cryptocurrency or Bitcoin Exchange: _____

Wallet address: _____

Currency Type (e.g. Bitcoin, Ethereum, Solana, Tron etc.): _____

Balance: _____

Private Key: _____

Public Key: _____

Online Login URL: _____

Online Login Username: _____

Online Login Password: _____

Retirement Accounts (e.g. 401(k), IRA)

Retirement accounts, such as 401(k)s and IRAs, are important financial assets that can help provide for Person 1's financial needs during retirement. In the context of a personal information document, information related to retirement accounts can include the types of accounts that Person 1 has, the account numbers, the names and contact information for the financial institutions that hold the accounts, and any beneficiary information.

Having this information readily available can help to ensure that Person 1's retirement accounts are properly managed and protected. It can also be useful for estate planning purposes, as Person 1 may want to designate specific beneficiaries to receive the funds in the event of their death.

It's important to note that retirement accounts are subject to specific rules and regulations, such as required minimum distributions (RMDs) and early withdrawal penalties. Therefore, it may be helpful for Person 1 to also include information about their retirement goals and plans, so that their beneficiaries or estate executor can make informed decisions about how to manage the accounts.

Account Holder(s): _____

Account Number(s): _____

Institution(s): _____

Beneficiary(ies): _____

Contribution Amount: _____

Investment Allocations: _____

Account Holder(s): _____

Account Number(s): _____

Institution(s): _____

Beneficiary(ies): _____

Contribution Amount: _____

Investment Allocations: _____

Account Holder(s): _____

Account Number(s): _____

Institution(s): _____

Beneficiary(ies): _____

Contribution Amount: _____

Investment Allocations: _____

Pension Plans

A pension plan is a type of retirement plan where an employer promises to pay a fixed amount of income to an employee after they retire. Pension plans are typically funded by the employer, although employees may also contribute to their own pension plan.

In a pension plan, the employer makes contributions to a fund on behalf of the employee, and the money is invested to generate income over time. When the employee reaches retirement age, they receive regular payments from the pension plan.

Pension plans can be either defined benefit plans or defined contribution plans. In a defined benefit plan, the employer guarantees the employee a specific amount of retirement income. In a defined contribution plan, the employer contributes a fixed amount to the employee's retirement account, and the employee is responsible for managing the investments and deciding how to withdraw the money in retirement.

It's important to keep track of pension plans and include them in your financial information in case of unexpected events such as disability or death, and to ensure that your beneficiaries receive the appropriate benefits.

Plan Name: _____

Plan Administrator: _____

Benefit Amount: _____

Payment Frequency: _____

Beneficiary(ies): _____

Vesting Information: _____

Pension Plan 2

Plan Name: _____

Plan Administrator: _____

Benefit Amount: _____

Payment Frequency: _____

Beneficiary(ies): _____

Vesting Information: _____

Pension Plan 3

Plan Name: _____

Plan Administrator: _____

Benefit Amount: _____

Payment Frequency: _____

Beneficiary(ies): _____

Vesting Information: _____

Stock Options

Stock options are a form of compensation given to employees by their employer, allowing them to buy company stock at a set price within a specific time frame. They are a type of financial instrument that gives the holder the right to buy or sell a specific amount of stock at a certain price, known as the strike price.

In the context of personal finance and estate planning, it is important to document any stock options that you may have, including the number of options, the strike price, and the expiration date. It is also important to document any beneficiaries or heirs who may be entitled to these options in the event of your death.

It is recommended to consult with a financial advisor or estate planning attorney to determine the best course of action for managing and distributing stock options as part of your estate plan.

Stock Options

Company Name: _____

Option Grant Date(s): _____

Option Expiration Date(s): _____

Number of Shares: _____

Strike Price: _____

Vesting Schedule: _____

Stock Options 2

Company Name: _____

Option Grant Date(s): _____

Option Expiration Date(s): _____

Number of Shares: _____

Strike Price: _____

Vesting Schedule: _____

Stock Options 3

Company Name: _____

Option Grant Date(s): _____

Option Expiration Date(s): _____

Number of Shares: _____

Strike Price: _____

Vesting Schedule: _____

Social Security Information

Social Security Information refers to the details related to an individual's Social Security benefits, including their Social Security number, benefit statement, and other relevant documentation.

The Social Security Administration (SSA) provides benefits to retired, disabled, or deceased individuals and their eligible dependents. To receive Social Security benefits, individuals must have a Social Security number, which is a unique nine-digit identification number issued by the SSA.

In addition to the Social Security number, individuals should keep a record of their Social Security benefit statement, which outlines their estimated future retirement, disability, and survivor benefits. It's important to review this statement periodically to ensure the information is accurate and up-to-date.

Individuals who are eligible for Social Security benefits should also keep track of any documentation related to their benefits, including their application for benefits and any correspondence with the SSA. This information can be crucial in case of any issues or disputes with the SSA.

Overall, including Social Security Information in an important document or an estate plan can help ensure that an individual's benefits are protected and allocated according to their wishes.

Social Security Number(s): _____

Statement(s) of Benefits: _____

Survivor Benefits: _____

Disability Benefits: _____

Trusts

A trust is a legal arrangement where an individual, known as the trustor or grantor, transfers their assets or property to a trustee, who manages and distributes the assets to the beneficiaries according to the terms outlined in the trust agreement. Trusts can be established for a variety of reasons, such as to avoid probate, minimize estate taxes, protect assets, and provide for beneficiaries.

In a trust, the trustor establishes the terms of the trust, including the beneficiaries, the assets to be included, and the rules for distribution. The trustee, who can be an individual or a financial institution, manages the trust assets and ensures that they are distributed according to the trust terms. The beneficiaries are the individuals or organizations who receive the benefits of the trust, such as income or assets.

There are several types of trusts, including revocable living trusts, irrevocable trusts, charitable trusts, and special needs trusts. The type of trust chosen will depend on the specific goals and needs of the trustor.

It is important to include information about trusts in an estate plan so that beneficiaries are aware of their existence and can receive the benefits intended for them. This can include details about the assets included in the trust, the trustee's contact information, and instructions for how the trust should be managed and distributed.

Trust Name: _____

Trustee(s): _____

Beneficiary(ies): _____

Trust Assets: _____

Trust Terms and Conditions: _____

Trust Name: _____

Trustee(s): _____

Beneficiary(ies): _____

Trust Assets: _____

Trust Terms and Conditions: _____

Trust Name: _____

Trustee(s): _____

Beneficiary(ies): _____

Trust Assets: _____

Trust Terms and Conditions: _____

Business Interest

Business interest refers to an individual's ownership in a business or businesses. This can include sole proprietorships, partnerships, limited liability companies (LLCs), and corporations. In the context of an estate plan, an individual may have business interests that need to be addressed in their will or other legal documents.

It is important to provide details of the business interests in the estate plan, such as the name of the business, the type of ownership interest, and any relevant financial information. This can help ensure that the business interest is handled in accordance with the individual's wishes after they pass away.

For example, if an individual owns a significant percentage of a family business, they may want to specify in their will how their interest in the business should be distributed among family members or other heirs. Alternatively, they may want to provide instructions for the sale or transfer of the business interest after their death.

Business interests can also have tax implications, so it is important to consult with an attorney or financial advisor when including them in an estate plan.

Business Name: _____

Business Type: _____

Percentage of Ownership: _____

Value of Ownership: _____

Business Contacts: _____

Business Documents: _____

Business Name: _____

Business Type: _____

Percentage of Ownership: _____

Value of Ownership: _____

Business Contacts: _____

Business Documents: _____

Business Name: _____

Business Type: _____

Percentage of Ownership: _____

Value of Ownership: _____

Business Contacts: _____

Business Documents: _____

Vehicle(s)

Sure, when it comes to the section on vehicles in a personal information document, it typically includes information on any vehicles that belong to the individual, including cars, trucks, motorcycles, boats, and other types of vehicles.

Some of the information that may be included in this section can include:

- The make, model, year, and color of each vehicle

- The license plate number and state

- The vehicle identification number (VIN)

- The current location of the vehicle

- The estimated value of the vehicle

- Any outstanding loans or liens on the vehicle

Having this information in a personal information document can be helpful in case of an emergency, such as a car accident, or if the individual becomes unable to manage their affairs due to illness or incapacity. It can also be useful when it comes to estate planning, as the information can be used to ensure that the individual's assets are distributed according to their wishes after their passing.

Vehicle: _____

Value: _____

(VIN):

Vehicle Id Number: _____

License Plate Number: _____

Annual Registration: _____

Auto Insurance

Account Number: _____

Due Date: _____

Amount: _____

Payment Method: _____

Notes: _____

Vehicle: _____

Value: _____

(VIN):

Vehicle Id Number: _____

License Plate Number: _____

Annual Registration: _____

Auto Insurance

Account Number: _____

Due Date: _____

Amount: _____

Payment Method: _____

Notes: _____

Vehicle(s) Continued

In the context of personal information management, the section on vehicle(s) typically includes information on all owned vehicles, including cars, trucks, motorcycles, RVs, and boats. This information may include the make and model of the vehicle, the year it was manufactured, its license plate number, registration information, and any loans or liens against the vehicle.

Other important details that may be included in this section are the vehicle identification number (VIN), purchase price, insurance information, and maintenance records. It may also be helpful to include any upgrades or modifications made to the vehicle, as well as its current value.

Having this information readily available can be useful in a variety of situations, such as when applying for car insurance, selling the vehicle, or filing a police report in case of theft. Additionally, keeping track of maintenance and repairs can help ensure the vehicle stays in good condition and maintains its value.

Vehicle: _____

Value: _____

(VIN): _____

Vehicle Id Number: _____

License Plate Number: _____

Annual Registration: _____

Auto Insurance

Account Number: _____

Due Date: _____

Amount: _____

Payment Method: _____

Notes: _____

Vehicle: _____

Value: _____

(VIN): _____

Vehicle Id Number: _____

License Plate Number: _____

Annual Registration: _____

Auto Insurance

Account Number: _____

Due Date: _____

Amount: _____

Payment Method: _____

Notes: _____

Real Estate and Property

Real estate and property refer to any land, buildings, or other physical assets that a person owns. This can include:

- **Home:** This refers to the primary residence of the person. The information can include the address, the purchase price, mortgage information, and other relevant details.

- **Rental Properties:** If a person owns rental properties, they should include information such as the address, rental income, expenses, and mortgage information.

- **Land:** This can include any undeveloped property, such as a plot of land that a person owns. The information should include the location, the size, and any relevant details about the property.

- **Vehicles:** This section can include information about any vehicles that the person owns, such as cars, motorcycles, boats, or recreational vehicles. The information should include the make, model, year, and any relevant details about the vehicle, such as the registration number, insurance information, and maintenance history.

- **Other Assets:** This section can include any other assets that the person owns, such as artwork, jewelry, or collectibles. The information should include the value, location, and any relevant details about the asset.

Home: _____

Asset Type: _____

Value: _____

Location: _____

Ownership Details: _____

Home: _____

Asset Type: _____

Value: _____

Location: _____

Ownership Details: _____

Home: _____

Asset Type: _____

Value: _____

Location: _____

Ownership Details: _____

Rental or Vacation Property

Rental or vacation property refers to any real estate property that an individual owns but does not reside in full-time. It can include a second home, a vacation property, or a rental property.

When creating a document that includes rental or vacation property information, it is important to include the property address, the type of property (such as a condo, townhome, or single-family home), and the current status of the property (whether it is rented out or available for use).

In addition, it can be helpful to include any rental agreements or contracts associated with the property, as well as contact information for any property management companies or rental agents. If the property is rented out, include the rental income and any associated expenses, such as mortgage payments, property taxes, insurance, and maintenance costs.

It is also important to include information on any outstanding mortgages or loans on the property, as well as the current market value of the property. This information can be helpful in making decisions about the property's future, such as whether to sell or continue to rent it out.

Home: _____

Asset Type: _____

Value: _____

Location: _____

Ownership Details: _____

Home: _____

Asset Type: _____

Value: _____

Location: _____

Ownership Details: _____

Home: _____

Asset Type: _____

Value: _____

Location: _____

Ownership Details: _____

Home: _____

Asset Type: _____

Value: _____

Location: _____

Ownership Details: _____

Property 1

"Property 1" usually refers to a specific property or asset that an individual owns or has an interest in. This can include a primary residence, a vacation home, rental property, land, or commercial real estate.

In an important documents binder, the section for "Property 1" would typically include information such as the property address, ownership details, purchase price or current value, mortgage or lien information, and any other relevant details. This section may also include copies of deeds, titles, or other legal documents related to the property.

It is important to keep this information up-to-date and easily accessible in case it is needed for legal or financial reasons.

Type of Property (Apartment, Condo,
House, Land, etc.): _____

Location: _____

Value: _____

Ownership (e.g.
Joint, Husband, Wife): _____

Mortgage Details

Property Mortgage: _____

Lender: _____

Loan Amount: _____

Interest Rate: _____

Term: _____

Monthly Payment: _____

Taxes

Annual Property Tax: _____

Due Date: _____

Maintenance and Repairs: _____

Rental Information

Rental information is typically related to a property that is being rented out to tenants. This information may include details about the property, such as the address, square footage, number of bedrooms and bathrooms, and amenities.

It may also include information about the rental agreement, such as the monthly rent amount, lease term, security deposit, and any other fees or charges associated with renting the property.

Other rental information may include details about the current tenants, such as their names, contact information, and payment history. Landlords may also keep records of maintenance and repairs that have been performed on the property, as well as any issues or complaints that have been reported by tenants.

Overall, rental information is important for both landlords and tenants to keep track of to ensure a smooth and successful rental experience.

Property Name: _____

Property Address: _____

Monthly Rental Income: _____

Tenant Name: _____

Contact Information: _____

Lease Start Date: _____ Lease End Date: _____

Notes or Comments About the Rental Income: _____

_____

_____

Property 2

"Property 2" generally refers to a second piece of real estate or property that the individual owns. This section of the personal information document can include details such as the property's location, the type of property (e.g., residential, commercial), the size of the property, the current market value or purchase price, any outstanding mortgage or liens, and other relevant information about the property. Additionally, this section can also include information on any rental income generated by the property, as well as any associated expenses such as property taxes, insurance, and maintenance costs.

Type of Property (Apartment, Condo,

House, Land, etc.): _____

Location: _____

Value: _____

Ownership (e.g.

Joint, Husband, Wife): _____

Mortgage Details

Property Mortgage: _____

Lender: _____

Loan Amount: _____

Interest Rate: _____

Term: _____

Monthly Payment: _____

Taxes

Annual Property Tax: _____

Due Date: _____

Maintenance and Repairs: _____

Rental Information

Rental information for Property 2 may include details such as:

- **Rental Agreement:** This is a legally binding contract between the landlord and the tenant that outlines the terms and conditions of the rental, including the rental amount, payment due date, lease duration, security deposit, late payment fees, pet policies, maintenance and repairs, and more.

- **Rent Payment:** This section includes details on how much rent is due each month, the payment due date, accepted payment methods, and penalties for late or missed payments.

- **Security Deposit:** This is the amount of money that the tenant pays upfront to the landlord to cover any damages or unpaid rent at the end of the lease. The security deposit amount, terms of use, and refund conditions should be detailed in this section.

- **Utilities:** Information about which utilities are included in the rent, such as water, gas, and electricity, and which ones the tenant is responsible for paying.

- **Maintenance and Repairs:** This section outlines who is responsible for maintenance and repairs, and how requests for repairs should be submitted and handled.

- **Move-In and Move-Out:** This section details the process for moving in and out of the rental property, including any move-in or move-out fees, required cleaning, and procedures for returning keys.

- **Tenant Rights and Responsibilities:** This section outlines the tenant's rights and responsibilities, including the right to quiet enjoyment, the obligation to keep the property clean and undamaged, and restrictions on alterations or modifications.

- **Landlord Rights and Responsibilities:** This section outlines the landlord's rights and responsibilities, such as the right to enter the rental property for inspections or repairs, and the obligation to provide a habitable living environment.

- **Termination of Lease:** This section outlines the terms and conditions for terminating the lease, including notice requirements, penalties for breaking the lease, and procedures for returning the security deposit.

Homeowners Insurance

Homeowners insurance is a type of insurance policy that protects a homeowner's property and belongings in case of damage or loss due to various incidents. This insurance typically covers damage from natural disasters like fire, wind, hail, lightning, and theft, as well as damage to personal property inside the home.

Homeowners insurance policies can vary in terms of coverage and price, and may also include liability coverage for injuries that occur on the property. It is usually required by mortgage lenders as a condition of approving a home loan.

When purchasing homeowners insurance, it is important to carefully review the policy to understand what is covered and what is not. Homeowners should also regularly review and update their policy as needed, and ensure they have adequate coverage to protect their home and assets.

Account Name: _____

Account Number: _____

Due Date: _____ Amount: _____

Payment Method: _____

Account Number: _____

Notes: _____

Account Name: _____

Account Number: _____

Due Date: _____ Amount: _____

Payment Method: _____

Account Number: _____

Notes: _____

Monthly Utilities Property 1

Monthly utilities for a property typically refer to the regular expenses related to essential services such as water, electricity, gas, internet, and cable TV. This information is important to have in a personal information document as it provides an overview of the ongoing expenses that need to be paid to maintain the property. It can also be helpful for budgeting purposes and to ensure that payments are made on time.

Electricity

Account Name: _____

Account Number: _____

Due Date: _____ Amount: _____

Payment Method: _____

Account Number: _____

Notes: _____

Gas/Oil

Account Name: _____

Account Number: _____

Due Date: _____ Amount: _____

Payment Method: _____

Account Number: _____

Notes: _____

Garbage

Account Name: _____

Account Number: _____

Due Date: _____ Amount: _____

Payment Method: _____

Account Number: _____

Notes: _____

Water / Sewer

Account Name: _____

Account Number: _____

Due Date: _____ Amount: _____

Payment Method: _____

Account Number: _____

Notes: _____

Monthly Utilities Property 2

Monthly Utilities for Property 2 refers to the regular bills and expenses related to the property, such as:

- **Electricity:** This includes the cost of using electricity to power the property. The cost of electricity can vary depending on the location and usage.

- **Water:** This includes the cost of using water in the property, including drinking water, wastewater, and any irrigation systems.

- **Gas:** If the property has gas appliances or heating, then there will be a gas bill associated with it. Gas costs can vary depending on usage and location.

- **Internet and Cable:** This includes the cost of any internet and cable services used in the property. The cost of these services can vary depending on the provider and the package selected.

- **Home Security:** If the property has a home security system, there will be a monthly cost associated with it.

- **Waste Disposal:** This includes the cost of trash and recycling services for the property.

- **Homeowner's Association (HOA) fees:** If the property is part of an HOA, there will be monthly fees associated with it. These fees can vary depending on the location and services provided.

- **Property Insurance:** This includes the cost of insuring the property against damages and liabilities.

The amount of these expenses can vary depending on the location and the usage of the property.

Electricity

Account Name: _____

Account Number: _____

Due Date: _____   Amount: _____

Payment Method: _____

Account Number: _____

Notes: _____

Gas/Oil

Account Name: _____

Account Number: _____

Due Date: _____   Amount: _____

Payment Method: _____

Account Number: _____

Notes: _____

Garbage

Account Name: _____

Account Number: _____

Due Date: _____ Amount: _____

Payment Method: _____

Account Number: _____

Notes: _____

Water / Sewer

Account Name: _____

Account Number: _____

Due Date: _____ Amount: _____

Payment Method: _____

Account Number: _____

Notes: _____

Monthly Utilities Property 3

As mentioned earlier, the "Monthly Utilities" subsection typically includes information on the various utility services used by the individual and their corresponding monthly costs. For "Property 3", this would likely include the following:

- **Electricity:** The amount paid each month for the property's electricity usage.

- **Water:** The monthly cost of water usage for the property.

- **Gas:** If the property uses gas for heating or other appliances, the monthly cost would be listed here.

- **Internet/cable/phone:** This would include any monthly charges for internet, cable TV, and/or phone services.

- **Trash:** The cost of waste management and trash pickup for the property.

The specific details and amounts for each utility service would be listed under their respective categories.

Electricity

Account Name: _____

Account Number: _____

Due Date: _____ Amount: _____

Payment Method: _____

Account Number: _____

Notes: _____

Gas/Oil

Account Name: _____

Account Number: _____

Due Date: _____ Amount: _____

Payment Method: _____

Account Number: _____

Notes: _____

Garbage

Account Name: _____

Account Number: _____

Due Date: _____ Amount: _____

Payment Method: _____

Account Number: _____

Notes: _____

Water / Sewer

Account Name: _____

Account Number: _____

Due Date: _____ Amount: _____

Payment Method: _____

Account Number: _____

Notes: _____

Miscellaneous Discretionary Home Expenses

Miscellaneous discretionary home expenses refer to any regular, non-essential expenses that are associated with the home or household. These expenses can vary depending on individual preferences and lifestyle choices. Some common examples of miscellaneous discretionary home expenses are:

- **Internet:** Monthly fees for home internet service, such as cable or fiber optic.

- **Cable:** Monthly fees for cable TV service, which may include access to premium channels or on-demand programming.

- **Streaming services:** Monthly subscription fees for streaming services, such as Netflix, Hulu, or Disney+.

- **Subscriptions (Newspapers/Magazines):** Monthly or annual fees for subscriptions to newspapers or magazines.

- **Gym membership:** Monthly or annual fees for access to a gym or fitness center.

- **Other recurring payments:** Other regular expenses that may be associated with the home, such as landscaping or cleaning services, pet care, or home security services.

It is important to keep track of these expenses as they can add up over time and have a significant impact on personal finances. By including these expenses in a personal record or financial plan, individuals can better manage their budgets and make informed decisions about their discretionary spending.

Account Name: _____

Account Number: _____

Due Date: _____ Amount: _____

Payment Method: _____

Account Number: _____

Notes: _____

Account Name: _____

Account Number: _____

Due Date: _____ Amount: _____

Payment Method: _____

Account Number: _____

Notes: _____

Miscellaneous Discretionary Home Expenses Continued

- Home security system

- Landscaping and lawn care

- Pool maintenance

- Pest control services

- Cleaning services

- Home repairs and maintenance

- Home renovation or improvement projects

- HOA fees

- Property taxes

- Home insurance premiums

- Energy-efficient upgrades

- Furniture and decor purchases

- Artwork and collectibles

- Electronics and gadgets

- Hobby or sports equipment

- Clothing and accessories storage or maintenance (such as dry cleaning)

- Special occasion expenses (such as birthday or holiday decorations)

- Personal care services (such as hairstyling or manicures)

- Entertainment expenses (such as movie or concert ticket)

Chapter 2:

HEALTH & MEDICAL INFORMATION

———

The section of Health & Medical Information is an important part of a personal information document that provides information about a person's medical history, current health status, and future health care preferences. This information is important for medical professionals in case of emergency situations or if a person is unable to make medical decisions for themselves.

The subsections for this section can include:

- **Medical Conditions:** This section lists any medical conditions a person has, such as diabetes, heart disease, allergies, etc. It is important to provide details on the type of condition, the date of diagnosis, and any current treatments.

- **Medications:** This section lists all current medications a person is taking, including over-the-counter medications, vitamins, and supplements. It should include the medication name, dosage, and frequency.

- **Allergies:** This section lists any allergies a person has, including food allergies, drug allergies, and environmental allergies.

- **Medical Procedures:** This section lists any medical procedures a person has undergone, such as surgeries, biopsies, or other medical treatments. It should include the date of the procedure, the name of the procedure, and the name of the doctor who performed it.

- **Medical Providers:** This section provides a list of medical providers a person has seen, including doctors, dentists, and other healthcare professionals. It should include the name of the provider, the type of provider, and their contact information.

- **Health Insurance:** This section provides information about a person's health insurance, including the name of the insurance provider, policy number, and contact information. It is important to keep this information up-to-date in case of any changes.

- **Advance Directives:** This section provides information about any advance directives a person has in place, such as a living will or a durable power of attorney for healthcare. These documents outline a person's preferences for medical treatment in case they become unable to make decisions for themselves.

Overall, the Health & Medical Information section is essential for anyone who wants to ensure that their medical needs and preferences are known in case of an emergency situation. It can help medical professionals provide the best possible care and treatment for the person, and give peace of mind to their loved ones.

Full Name: _____

Date of Birth: _____   Blood Type: _____

Height: _____   Weight: _____

Notes: _____

Medical Insurance Information

Insurance Provider: _____

Policy Number: _____

Group Number: _____

Phone Number: _____

Primary Care Physician: _____

Pharmacy: _____

Pharmacy Address: _____

Pharmacy Phone Number: _____

Notes: _____

Medical History

Medical history refers to a record of an individual's past and current health conditions, illnesses, surgeries, hospitalizations, allergies, medications, and treatments. This information is important for healthcare providers to make informed decisions about an individual's care, as it helps them understand any existing medical conditions, potential complications, and any medications or treatments that may interact with the current course of treatment.

When documenting medical history, it is important to include details such as the name of the condition, date of diagnosis, severity, medications taken, treatments received, and any hospitalizations or surgeries related to the condition. It is also important to document any allergies or adverse reactions to medications or treatments.

Medical history can be divided into several categories, including personal medical history, family medical history, and social history. Personal medical history refers to an individual's own health history, while family medical history refers to the health history of blood relatives. Social history includes information about an individual's lifestyle habits such as smoking, alcohol consumption, and exercise habits, as these factors can impact an individual's overall health.

It is important to keep an updated and accurate medical history record, as this can help healthcare providers make informed decisions about an individual's care and potentially prevent medical errors or complications.

Chronic Illnesses/Conditions: _____

    Continued: _____

    Continued: _____

    Continued: _____

    Continued: _____

Surgeries or Hospitalizations: _____

    Continued: _____

    Continued: _____

    Continued: _____

    Continued: _____

Family Medical History: _____

    Continued: _____

    Continued: _____

    Continued: _____

    Continued: _____

Medication Allergies: _____

    Continued: _____

    Continued: _____

    Continued: _____

    Continued: _____

Current Medications: _____

    Continued: _____

    Continued: _____

    Continued: _____

    Continued: _____

Medical Emergency(s)

Medical Emergency(s) refer to any unexpected or life-threatening medical situation that may arise, and the steps to be taken to address them. In this section of a personal information document, individuals may provide information on their medical emergency contacts, including their primary care physician, emergency contact person(s), and any other pertinent information that could be useful in the event of a medical emergency. This information may include details on allergies, medications, ongoing medical treatments, and any other medical issues that may require immediate attention. By providing this information, individuals can ensure that their medical needs are addressed promptly and efficiently, even if they are unable to communicate their needs directly. This information can also be useful to medical personnel during an emergency, providing them with crucial information to make informed decisions about a person's medical care.

Emergency Contacts (1)

Name: _____

Relationship: _____

Address: _____

Phone Number: _____

Emergency Contacts (2)

Name: _____

Relationship: _____

Address: _____

Phone Number: _____

Primary Care Physician

Clinic Name: _____

Physician Name: _____

Assistant's Name: _____

Address: _____

Phone Number: _____

Notes: _____

Secondary Care Physician

Clinic Name: _____

Physician Name: _____

Assistant's Name: _____

Address: _____

Phone Number: _____

Notes: _____

Medical Specialists

Medical Specialists refer to healthcare professionals who have specialized education and training in a particular area of medicine or surgery. They are experts in their field and can diagnose, treat and manage complex medical conditions related to their area of expertise. Some examples of medical specialists include:

- **Cardiologists:** A cardiologist specializes in diagnosing and treating heart diseases and conditions related to the cardiovascular system.

- **Neurologists:** A neurologist specializes in the diagnosis and treatment of diseases and conditions that affect the brain, spinal cord, and nervous system.

- **Oncologists:** An oncologist specializes in the diagnosis and treatment of cancer.

- **Gastroenterologists:** A gastroenterologist specializes in diagnosing and treating conditions related to the digestive system, including the esophagus, stomach, intestines, liver, and pancreas.

- **Endocrinologists:** An endocrinologist specializes in the diagnosis and treatment of disorders related to hormones and the endocrine system, including diabetes, thyroid disorders, and hormonal imbalances.

- **Pulmonologists:** A pulmonologist specializes in the diagnosis and treatment of conditions related to the respiratory system, including asthma, chronic obstructive pulmonary disease (COPD), and lung cancer.

- **Rheumatologists:** A rheumatologist specializes in the diagnosis and treatment of autoimmune disorders and conditions related to joints, muscles, and bones, such as arthritis.

- **Dermatologists:** A dermatologist specializes in the diagnosis and treatment of conditions related to the skin, hair, and nails, including acne, eczema, and psoriasis.

- **Psychiatrists:** A psychiatrist specializes in the diagnosis and treatment of mental health disorders, including depression, anxiety, and bipolar disorder.

It's important to have a list of medical specialists you or your family members regularly see to ensure prompt medical attention and care when needed.

Specialists (1)

Clinic Name: _____

Physician Name: _____

Address: _____

Phone Number: _____

Reason for Specialist: _____

Specialists (2)

Clinic Name: _____

Physician Name: _____

Address: _____

Phone Number: _____

Reason for Specialist: _____

Specialists (3)

Clinic Name: _____

Physician Name: _____

Address: _____

Phone Number: _____

Reason for Specialist: _____

Specialists (4)

Clinic Name: _____

Physician Name: _____

Address: _____

Phone Number: _____

Other Medical Providers

Other medical providers refer to health professionals who are not medical specialists but still provide essential medical services. These may include primary care physicians, nurse practitioners, physician assistants, chiropractors, physical therapists, occupational therapists, speech therapists, and mental health professionals such as psychologists and psychiatrists.

It is important to include contact information for all medical providers in this section so that they can be easily reached in case of emergencies or for routine appointments. It is also essential to keep this information updated regularly, especially if there are any changes in the medical provider's contact information or if a new provider is added to the list.

Dental

Insurance Provider: _____

Policy Number: _____

Clinic Name: _____

Dentist Name: _____

Assistant's Name: _____

Address: _____

Phone Number: _____

Notes: _____

Vision

Insurance Provider: _____

Policy Number: _____

Clinic Name: _____

Optometrist Name: _____

Assistant's Name: _____

Address: _____

Phone Number: _____

Notes: _____

Mental Health

Insurance Provider: _____

Policy Number: _____

Clinic Name: _____

Therapist Name: _____

Assistant's Name: _____

Address: _____

Phone Number: _____

Notes: _____

Living Will: (Yes/No)

Agent Name: _____

Durable Power of Attorney for Health Care: (Yes/No)

Name of Power of Attorney for Medical Decisions: _____

Physician Orders for Life-Sustaining Treatment (POLST)   (Yes/No)

Do Not Resuscitate Orders (DNR):   (Yes/No)

Organ Donor: (Yes/No)

Exceptions: _____

Tissue Donor: (Yes/No)

Exceptions: _____

Advance Directives

Advance directives are legal documents that allow individuals to make decisions about their future medical care, in case they become unable to do so themselves. Advance directives usually come into play if a person is terminally ill or permanently unconscious. There are several types of advance directives, including:

- **Living Will:** A living will is a document that outlines a person's wishes for end-of-life medical care. It specifies the types of medical treatments a person wants or does not want if they become unable to make decisions for themselves.

- **Durable Power of Attorney for Health Care:** A durable power of attorney for health care allows a person to appoint someone else to make medical decisions for them if they become unable to do so themselves. This person is called a healthcare proxy or agent.

- **Do Not Resuscitate (DNR) Order:** A DNR order is a medical order that instructs healthcare providers not to perform cardiopulmonary resuscitation (CPR) in the event of cardiac or respiratory arrest.

It is important for individuals to discuss their end-of-life wishes with their loved ones and healthcare providers and to ensure that their advance directives are up to date and legally valid.

Chapter 3:

MEDICATIONS TO-GO PAGE

———

A Medications To-Go Page is a document that contains important information about the medications a person is currently taking or has been prescribed. This page is usually kept in a portable format, such as a card or small booklet, that can be easily carried by the person in case of an emergency or when visiting a healthcare provider.

The information typically included on a Medications To-Go Page may include the person's name, date of birth, and contact information, as well as a list of all prescription medications they are taking, including the name of the medication, dosage, frequency, and the reason for taking it. It may also include a list of over-the-counter medications, vitamins, or supplements the person is taking.

Having a Medications To-Go Page can be particularly useful when a person is visiting a new healthcare provider, traveling, or in an emergency situation where they are unable to communicate their medical history and current medications. It can help healthcare providers make informed decisions about treatment, avoid potentially harmful drug interactions, and ensure that the person receives appropriate care.

Medication Name: _____

Purpose: _____

Dosage: _____

Date Last Filled: _____

Prescribing Physician: _____

Medication Name: _____

Purpose: _____

Dosage: _____

Date Last Filled: _____

Prescribing Physician: _____

Medication Name: _____

Purpose: _____

Dosage: _____

Date Last Filled: _____

Prescribing Physician: _____

Medication Name: _____

Purpose: _____

Dosage: _____

Date Last Filled: _____

Prescribing Physician: _____

Medication Name: _____

Purpose: _____

Dosage: _____

Date Last Filled: _____

Prescribing Physician: _____

Medication Name: _____

Purpose: _____

Dosage: _____

Date Last Filled: _____

Prescribing Physician: _____

Medication Name: _____

Purpose: _____

Dosage: _____

Date Last Filled: _____

Prescribing Physician: _____

Medication Name: _____

Purpose: _____

Dosage: _____

Date Last Filled: _____

Prescribing Physician: _____

Medication Name: _____

Purpose: _____

Dosage: _____

Date Last Filled: _____

Prescribing Physician: _____

Note: Please make sure to update this list regularly and keep it with you at all times in case of emergencies.

Chapter 4:

PASSWORDS & PROTECTED INFORMATION

———

To elaborate, the Passwords & Protected Information section of a personal organizer is a place to keep track of all your electronic passwords and login credentials for online accounts and services, such as email accounts, social media accounts, online banking, and other digital services. This section should be kept secure and should only be accessible to individuals authorized to access it.

It's essential to update the passwords and login credentials regularly to prevent unauthorized access to your accounts. You may also want to consider using a password manager to generate and store complex passwords securely.

It's important to note that including sensitive information like passwords in a physical personal organizer carries some risks. If you lose the organizer or it falls into the wrong hands, your personal information could be compromised. To mitigate this risk, you may want to consider storing your electronic passwords and login credentials in an encrypted digital file or using a secure password manager with two-factor authentication.

Electronic Passwords and Online Accounts

In this section of a personal information organizer, you can record all of your usernames and passwords for online accounts and digital services. This can include things like email accounts, social media accounts, online banking and investment accounts, e-commerce sites, and more. It's important to keep this information up to date and secure, as it can be a valuable target for hackers or other cyber threats.

Some tips for managing your electronic passwords and online accounts include:

- **Use unique, strong passwords for each account:** Avoid using the same password for multiple accounts, and use a mix of letters, numbers, and special characters to create strong passwords.

- **Enable two-factor authentication:** Many online services now offer two-factor authentication, which requires an additional code or prompt to access your account, in addition to your password.

- **Use a password manager:** Consider using a password manager to securely store and generate strong passwords for your accounts.

- **Update your passwords regularly:** Make sure to update your passwords every few months, or immediately if you suspect that an account may have been compromised.

- **Be cautious with sharing login information:** Avoid sharing your login information with others, and only provide it when necessary and to trusted sources.

Please fill in the information as applicable.

Email

Email is a system for exchanging messages electronically over a computer network, typically the internet. It allows users to send and receive messages, attachments, and other types of digital content to one or more recipients. Email can be accessed through various platforms such as web-based clients, desktop clients, and mobile apps, and it has become an essential tool for communication in both personal and professional settings. Some of the most popular email services include Gmail, Yahoo Mail, and Microsoft Outlook.

URL: _____

Type of Account: _____

Username: _____

Password: _____

Notes: _____

Email Continued

In addition to the email account credentials, this section may also include information on email providers, email settings, and other related details. Here are some examples of what can be included:

- **Email provider:** This refers to the company or service that provides the email account, such as Google, Microsoft, or Yahoo.

- **Email address:** The email address associated with the account.

- **Username:** Some email services require a username in addition to the email address.

- **Password:** The password associated with the account. It's important to keep this information secure and up to date.

- **Email settings:** This includes information on how the email account is set up, such as the incoming and outgoing server settings, port numbers, and encryption settings.

- **Email forwarding:** If you have set up email forwarding to another email address, it's important to include this information.

- **Spam filter settings:** This includes information on how the email service filters spam and unwanted messages.

- **Recovery options:** Some email services provide recovery options, such as security questions or a secondary email address, in case you forget your password or get locked out of your account.

It's important to keep this information up to date and secure, as email accounts often contain sensitive and confidential information.

URL: _____

Type of Account: _____

Username: _____

Password: _____

Notes: _____

URL: _____

Type of Account: _____

Username: _____

Password: _____

Notes: _____

URL: _____

Type of Account: _____

Username: _____

Password: _____

Notes: _____

URL: _____

Type of Account: _____

Username: _____

Password: _____

Notes: _____

Online Shopping

The "Online Shopping" subsection of "Electronic Passwords and Online Accounts" refers to any accounts you may have with online retailers or e-commerce websites. This could include accounts with Amazon, eBay, Walmart, or any other online store you regularly use to purchase goods or services. It's important to keep track of the login credentials for these accounts so you can easily access them and manage your orders. Additionally, you may want to keep track of any payment methods you have stored on these sites for quick and easy checkout.

URL: _____

Type of Account: _____

Username: _____

Password: _____

Notes: _____

URL: _____

Type of Account: _____

Username: _____

Password: _____

Notes: _____

URL: _____

Type of Account: _____

Username: _____

Password: _____

Notes: _____

Social Media

Social media refers to online platforms and tools that enable users to create, share, and participate in online communities or networks. These platforms allow users to create and share content, interact with others, and follow accounts or pages of interest.

In the context of a personal record or information, listing social media accounts can be helpful in case of emergencies or as a reference for loved ones who may need to access your accounts. It may also be useful for estate planning purposes to have a comprehensive list of all your online profiles and accounts.

Examples of social media platforms include Facebook, Twitter, Instagram, LinkedIn, Snapchat, and TikTok.

URL: _____

Type of Account: _____

Username: _____

Password: _____

Notes: _____

URL: _____

Type of Account: _____

Username: _____

Password: _____

Notes: _____

URL: _____

Type of Account: _____

Username: _____

Password: _____

Notes: _____

URL: _____

Type of Account: _____

Username: _____

Password: _____

Notes: _____

Medical Accounts Online

Medical accounts online refer to any online portals or websites related to your medical care, such as patient portals, health insurance portals, or telemedicine platforms. These platforms can provide access to important medical information, such as medical records, test results, appointment scheduling, and prescription refills. It is important to keep your login information for these accounts secure, as they may contain sensitive personal and medical information. You may also want to check with your healthcare provider to see what online portals or services they offer and how to access them securely.

URL: _____

Type of Account: _____

Username: _____

Password: _____

Notes: _____

URL: _____

Type of Account: _____

Username: _____

Password: _____

Notes: _____

URL: _____

Type of Account: _____

Username: _____

Password: _____

Notes: _____

URL: _____

Type of Account: _____

Username: _____

Password: _____

Notes: _____

URL: _____

Type of Account: _____

Username: _____

Password: _____

Notes: _____

Website / Service

In the context of passwords and protected information, the "Website / Service" section refers to any online service or website that you have an account with and may need to access in the future. This could include:

- Banking websites

- Investment accounts

- Insurance accounts

- Social media accounts

- Email accounts

- Online shopping accounts

- Streaming services

- Gaming accounts

- Educational accounts

- Healthcare accounts

- Government accounts

- Any other online accounts you use

For each website or service, you should include the following information:

- The name of the website or service

- Your username or login ID

- Your password

- Any additional security information, such as security questions or two-factor authentication settings

- Any notes or details about the account, such as the date it was created or the purpose of the account

It's important to keep this information secure, as it can provide access to your sensitive personal and financial information. You may want to consider using a password manager or other secure method to store this information. Additionally, be sure to update your passwords regularly and use strong, unique passwords for each account.

URL: _____

Type of Account: _____

Username: _____

Password: _____

Notes: _____

URL: _____

Type of Account: _____

Username: _____

Password: _____

Notes: _____

URL: _____

Type of Account: _____

Username: _____

Password: _____

Notes: _____

In addition to online accounts, you can also include any physical safes or safety deposit boxes that you have and their corresponding access information.

Safe/Safety Deposit Box

A safe deposit box is a secure container, typically located in a bank or a credit union, where people can store valuables, important documents, and other items that they want to protect from theft, fire, or natural disasters. The box is usually made of steel and can only be opened with a key or combination provided to the owner. The bank or credit union provides access to the box, typically during regular business hours, and may also provide insurance for the contents of the box.

People use safe deposit boxes to store a variety of items, such as important legal documents (e.g., birth certificates, wills, and deeds), family heirlooms, jewelry, and cash. Some people also use them to store copies of important data (e.g., photographs or computer backups) or other items that they don't want to keep at home.

It's important to note that safe deposit boxes are not FDIC-insured. This means that if the bank or credit union where you have a safe deposit box goes out of business or is robbed, you may not be able to recover the contents of your box. Therefore, it's a good idea to make sure that your valuables and important documents are also backed up and stored in a secure location at home or with a trusted family member or friend.

Type of Account: _____

Name on Account: _____

Access Information: _____

Location: _____

Notes: _____

Type of Account: _____

Name on Account: _____

Access Information: _____

Location: _____

Notes: _____

Type of Account: _____

Name on Account: _____

Access Information: _____

Location: _____

Notes: _____

Make sure to keep this information secure and share it only with trusted individuals. It's also important to update this information regularly as passwords and access information may change over time.

Chapter 5:

LEGAL DOCUMENTS
& INFORMATION

———

Legal Documents — Husband, Wife or Partner

Legal documents related to marriage or partnership may include:

- **Marriage certificate:** This is the document that legally proves you are married. It is typically issued by the state or county where you were married

- **Prenuptial agreement:** This is a legal document that outlines how assets and debts will be divided in the event of a divorce. It is signed before marriage.

- **Postnuptial agreement:** This is similar to a prenuptial agreement but is signed after marriage.

- **Will:** This legal document outlines how your assets will be distributed after your death.

- **Trust:** A trust is a legal arrangement that allows a third party (the trustee) to hold assets on behalf of a beneficiary.

- **Power of attorney:** This legal document grants someone the authority to act on your behalf in financial or legal matters.

- **Health care proxy:** This legal document designates someone to make medical decisions on your behalf if you are unable to do so.

It's important to keep these documents in a safe and secure location, such as a fireproof safe or safety deposit box at a bank. It's also a good idea to make copies and give them to trusted family members or an attorney. If any of these documents are lost or stolen, it's important to take steps to replace them as soon as possible.

(Be sure to replace lost or stolen documents)

Power of Attorney

Name of Attorney-in-Fact: _____

Location of Original Document: _____

Contact Information of Lawyer: _____

Living Will

Name of Proxy: _____

Treatment Preferences: _____

Location of Original Document: _____

Contact Information of Lawyer: _____

Will

Name of Executor: _____

Name of Beneficiaries: _____

Continued: _____

Continued: _____

Continued: _____

Continued: _____

Location of Original Document: _____

Contact Information of Lawyer: _____

Cohabitation Agreement

Date Signed: _____

Location of Original Document: _____

Contact Information of Lawyer: _____

Prenuptial Agreement

Date Signed: _____

Location of Original Document: _____

Contact Information of Lawyer: _____

Other Legal Documents

Here are some other legal documents that you may want to consider including in your records:

- **Wills and trusts:** These documents specify how you want your assets distributed after you die. You may also want to include any relevant documentation for trusts you have established.

- **Powers of attorney:** These documents designate a trusted individual to make decisions on your behalf in the event that you are unable to do so.

- **Living will:** This document outlines your wishes for end-of-life care and can provide guidance to your loved ones and medical professionals in the event of a medical emergency.

- **Property deeds and titles:** These documents prove ownership of real estate and other significant assets.

- **Marriage or divorce certificates:** These documents prove your marital status and can be important for things like obtaining government benefits or changing your name.

- **Adoption papers:** These documents are important if you have adopted a child, as they establish your legal relationship with the child.

- **Business formation documents:** If you own a business, you will want to include any relevant documentation such as articles of incorporation, partnership agreements, or operating agreements.

It is important to keep these documents in a safe and secure location, such as a fireproof safe or safety deposit box, and to make sure your loved ones know where to find them in the event of an emergency.

Description: _____

Location of Original Document: _____

Contact Information of Lawyer: _____

Notes: _____

_____

_____

Passport

A passport is an official government-issued document that verifies the identity and nationality of the person holding it. It is typically used for international travel, as it allows the holder to cross borders and enter foreign countries.

Passports usually contain the following information about the holder:

- Full name

- Date of birth

- Place of birth

- Passport number

- Photo of the holder

- Signature of the holder

- Expiration date

To obtain a passport, you must apply through the government agency responsible for issuing them in your country of citizenship. This typically involves filling out an application, providing identification and proof of citizenship, and paying a fee.

It's important to keep your passport in a safe and secure place, as losing it can be a significant inconvenience, and replacing it can be costly and time-consuming. Many people choose to store their passport in a safe or safety deposit box when not in use.

Passport Number: _____

Country of Origin: _____

Website: _____

Phone Number: _____

Where to Report Lost/Stolen: _____

Process to Replace: _____

_____

_____

Driver's License

A driver's license is an official government-issued document that authorizes an individual to operate a motor vehicle. It serves as proof of identity and establishes that the individual has completed the necessary requirements to legally operate a motor vehicle.

The requirements to obtain a driver's license may vary by state or country, but generally include a written exam, a driving skills test, and a vision test. The license typically needs to be renewed every few years and may require additional testing or documentation.

It's important to keep your driver's license information up to date and ensure that you have a valid license at all times when driving. If you lose your license or it gets stolen, it's important to report it to the appropriate authorities and take steps to obtain a replacement.

License Number: _____

State of Issuance: _____

Website: _____

Phone Number: _____

Where to Report Lost/Stolen: _____

Process to Replace: _____

Social Security Card

A Social Security card is a vital record that contains a unique nine-digit number assigned to every citizen, permanent resident, and temporary worker in the United States. The Social Security number (SSN) is used to track a person's earnings and work history to determine their eligibility for Social Security benefits. It is also used for tax purposes, to report wages and self-employment income to the Internal Revenue Service (IRS), and for other purposes such as opening bank accounts or applying for credit.

If you lose your Social Security card, you should request a replacement card from the Social Security Administration (SSA) as soon as possible. To obtain a replacement card, you will need to provide certain documents to prove your identity, age, and citizenship or immigration status. It's important to keep your Social Security card in a safe place and to avoid carrying it with you unless necessary to prevent identity theft.

Social Security Number: _____

State of Issuance: _____

Website: _____

Phone Number: _____

Where to Report Lost/Stolen: _____

Process to Replace: _____

_____

_____

Birth Certificate

A birth certificate is a legal document that serves as proof of a person's identity and citizenship. It includes information such as the individual's full name, date and place of birth, parents' names, and other vital information. Birth certificates are issued by the government in the state or country where the individual was born, and they are often required for a variety of purposes, including obtaining a passport, enrolling in school or the military, and applying for government benefits. It's important to keep a copy of your birth certificate in a safe and secure place, and to have an additional copy in case the original is lost or damaged.

License Number: _____

State of Issuance: _____

Website: _____

Phone Number: _____

Where to Report Lost/Stolen: _____

Process to Replace: _____

_____

_____

Mariage Certificate

A marriage certificate is a legal document that proves a couple is legally married. It typically includes the full names of both spouses, the date and location of the marriage, and the name and signature of the person who performed the ceremony. This document is typically issued by the county or state where the marriage took place. A marriage certificate can be important for a variety of reasons, such as

License Number: _____

State of Issuance: _____

Website: _____

Phone Number: _____

Where to Report Lost/Stolen: _____

Process to Replace: _____

_____

_____

Misc. Legal Document

Miscellaneous Legal Documents may include but are not limited to:

- **Power of Attorney:** A legal document that grants someone else the authority to act on your behalf for specific matters, such as financial, legal, or healthcare decisions.

- **Living Will/Advance Directive:** A legal document that allows you to specify your medical treatment preferences if you become unable to communicate.

- **Trusts:** A legal arrangement where a trustee holds and manages assets on behalf of a beneficiary.

- **Wills:** A legal document that outlines how you want your assets to be distributed after your death.

- **Property Deeds:** Legal documents that provide proof of ownership of real estate or property.

- **Vehicle Titles:** Legal documents that provide proof of ownership for vehicles.

- **Business Agreements:** Legal documents that outline the terms and conditions of a business transaction or partnership.

It's important to keep these documents safe and secure as they may be needed in legal or emergency situations. Make sure to inform trusted family members or an attorney about the location of these documents.

Misc. Legal Document: _____

Website: _____

Phone Number: _____

Where to Report Lost/Stolen: _____

Process to Replace: _____

_____

_____

Misc. Legal Document: _____

Website: _____

Phone Number: _____

Where to Report Lost/Stolen: _____

Process to Replace: _____

_____

_____

Chapter 6:

IMPORTANT CONTACTS

———

The "Important Contacts" section of a personal information organizer is where you can keep a list of key individuals and organizations that you may need to contact in case of an emergency or other situations. Some examples of contacts you may want to include in this section are:

- **Family members:** You may want to include the names and contact information of your immediate family members, such as parents, siblings, and children.

- **Close friends:** You may want to include the names and contact information of your close friends who you would want to be informed in case of an emergency.

- **Doctors and medical providers:** You should include the names and contact information of your primary care doctor and any other medical specialists you see regularly.

- **Emergency contacts:** This may include the contact information of people you would like to be notified in case of an emergency, such as a trusted neighbor or friend who can take care of your pets or check on your home.

- **Financial advisors and accountants:** You may want to include the contact information of your financial advisor, accountant, or tax preparer.

- **Insurance providers:** You should include the contact information for your various insurance providers, such as your health insurance, life insurance, and home insurance.

- **Legal professionals:** If you have a lawyer, you should include their contact information, as well as any other legal professionals you may work with, such as a notary public or executor of your will.

- **Utility companies**: You may want to include the contact information for your utility companies, such as your electric, gas, water, and phone providers.

- **Government agencies:** You may want to include the contact information for government agencies, such as your local city or county offices, as well as state and federal agencies that you may need to contact.

It's important to keep this section of your personal information organizer up to date, and to make sure that someone you trust knows where to find this information in case of an emergency.

Full Name: _____

Address: _____

City: _____

State: _____ Zip Code: _____

Country: _____

Phone: _____

eMail: _____

Relationship: _____

Full Name: _____

Address: _____

City: _____

Full Name: _____

Address: _____

City: _____

State: _____ Zip Code: _____

Country: _____

Phone: _____

eMail: _____

Relationship: _____

Full Name: _____

Address: _____

City: _____

State: _____ Zip Code: _____

Country: _____

Phone: _____

eMail: _____

Relationship: _____

Chapter 7:

IMPORTANT RESOURCES

Important resources refer to the essential contacts, information, and materials that you might need in case of an emergency or other unforeseen circumstances. These resources can include emergency services such as the police, fire department, and hospital, as well as utility companies, insurance providers, and financial institutions.

Some examples of important resources to include in your personal records include:

- **Emergency services:** This includes the phone numbers for the police, fire department, and hospital in your area. If you have specific emergency medical needs or allergies, be sure to include this information as well.

- **Utility companies:** In case of power outages, gas leaks, or other utility emergencies, it's essential to have the contact information for your local utility providers.

- **Insurance providers:** Be sure to include the contact information for your health, home, auto, and other insurance providers in case of an emergency or claim.

- **Financial institutions:** This includes the contact information for your bank, credit card companies, and any other financial institutions you work with. In case of a lost or stolen card, you will need to report it immediately.

- **Local government resources:** Depending on where you live, there may be other important resources to include in your personal records, such as the contact information for your local government offices or community organizations.

Overall, it's important to keep your important resources up to date and easily accessible in case of an emergency or other unforeseen circumstance. Regularly reviewing and updating this information can help ensure that you are prepared for any situation.

Department of Motor Vehicles

The Department of Motor Vehicles (DMV) is a government agency responsible for administering driver's licenses, vehicle registration, and other related services. The DMV is typically responsible for issuing and renewing driver's licenses and ID cards, as well as administering written and road tests. In addition, the DMV is also responsible for registering and titling vehicles, issuing license plates, and maintaining records related to ownership and registration. Some DMVs may also offer additional services, such as issuing disabled parking permits, conducting vehicle inspections, and providing information on traffic safety and regulations. The specific services offered by the DMV may vary by state or jurisdiction.

Department of Motor Vehicles (DMV)

Website for DMV Information

Phone Number for DMV Information

Application Process for Driver's License

Social Security

The Social Security Administration (SSA) is a government agency that administers Social Security benefits, a federal program that provides retirement, disability, and survivor benefits to eligible individuals. The SSA also administers the Supplemental Security Income (SSI) program, which provides financial assistance to individuals with disabilities, people over age 65, and certain other individuals who have limited income and resources.

To access your Social Security information, you can create an online account on the SSA website, which allows you to view your earnings record, estimate your future benefits, and manage your benefits. You can also contact the SSA by phone or visit a local Social Security office to get information about your benefits, apply for benefits, or get help with other Social Security-related issues.

Social Security Administration

Website for Social Security Information

Phone Number for Social Security Information

Application Process for Social Security Benefits

Taxes

Taxes are a mandatory financial obligation imposed by the government on individuals and businesses to fund public services and projects. There are several types of taxes, including income tax, sales tax, property tax, estate tax, and excise tax.

Income tax is a tax levied on an individual's earnings and is calculated based on a percentage of their income. Federal income tax is levied by the U.S. government, while state income tax is levied by individual states.

Sales tax is a tax levied on the sale of goods and services and is usually calculated as a percentage of the purchase price. Sales tax rates vary by state and locality.

Property tax is a tax levied on real estate and other property, such as vehicles or boats, and is calculated based on the assessed value of the property. Property taxes are usually paid to local governments, such as cities or counties.

Estate tax is a tax levied on the value of an individual's estate after they pass away. The tax is calculated based on the fair market value of the assets in the estate and is paid by the estate before it is distributed to the heirs.

Excise tax is a tax levied on the sale of specific goods or services, such as gasoline or tobacco products. The tax is usually included in the price of the goods or services and is paid by the consumer.

Taxes can be complex, and it is important to understand your tax obligations and how to properly file and pay them to avoid penalties and legal issues. It is recommended to seek the assistance of a tax professional or accountant to ensure compliance with tax laws and regulations.

Internal Revenue Service (IRS)

Website for Tax Information

Phone Number for Tax Information

_____

_____

_____

Application Process for Tax Returns

_____

_____

_____

Support Organizations

Support organizations are nonprofit groups that provide assistance, resources, and advocacy for individuals and families facing specific challenges or life situations. These organizations may focus on a particular health condition, disability, demographic group, or social issue.

Examples of support organizations include the American Cancer Society, which provides resources and support for cancer patients and their families, the National Alliance on Mental Illness (NAMI), which advocates for individuals living with mental health conditions and provides resources for support and treatment, and the National Organization for Rare Disorders (NORD), which provides information and advocacy for individuals living with rare diseases and their families.

Support organizations can provide a range of services, including education and awareness, advocacy and policy change, financial assistance and support, and peer support networks. They may also provide referrals to medical professionals, social services, or other relevant resources in the community.

If you or someone you know is facing a particular challenge or life situation, it may be helpful to research and connect with relevant support organizations to access resources, information, and support.

American Cancer Society

The American Cancer Society (ACS) is a nationwide, community-based voluntary health organization that aims to eliminate cancer by funding research, providing patient support, and raising awareness about cancer prevention and detection. The organization offers a variety of services and programs to support individuals and families affected by cancer, including free lodging for cancer patients and caregivers traveling for treatment, a 24/7 helpline, and support groups. The ACS also provides information and resources related to cancer prevention and early detection, including guidelines for cancer screenings, healthy lifestyle choices, and ways to reduce cancer risk. The organization relies on donations and volunteer efforts to support its mission.

Website for Cancer Resources

Phone Number for Cancer Resources

American Heart Association

The American Heart Association (AHA) is a non-profit organization that promotes cardiovascular health and aims to reduce disability and deaths caused by cardiovascular diseases and stroke. It was founded in 1924 and is headquartered in Dallas, Texas, with over 3,400 employees and more than 33 million volunteers and supporters.

The AHA provides a variety of services and resources to promote cardiovascular health, including education, advocacy, research funding, community programs, and public health campaigns. They offer resources and programs for healthcare professionals, patients, and the general public, including information on heart disease prevention, healthy lifestyle choices, CPR and emergency cardiovascular care training, and research on cardiovascular disease.

The AHA also hosts several fundraising events, such as the Heart Walk and Go Red for Women, which raise money for research, education, and public health initiatives. They collaborate with other organizations, healthcare providers, and government agencies to promote cardiovascular health and improve patient outcomes.

Website for Heart Health Resources

Phone Number for Heart Health Resources

Disability Support

Disability support refers to various resources and services available to people with disabilities to help them live as independently as possible and participate fully in their communities. These services can include medical care, assistive technologies, vocational rehabilitation, and accommodations in the workplace or school.

Some examples of disability support organizations include the National Council on Independent Living, which advocates for the rights of people with disabilities, and the National Organization on Disability, which provides information and resources for people with disabilities and their families.

In addition, many countries have government-funded disability support programs, such as Social Security Disability Insurance (SSDI) in the United States, which provides financial assistance to people with disabilities who are unable to work.

Overall, disability support is designed to help people with disabilities overcome barriers and achieve their goals, whether those goals involve independent living, education, or employment.

Organization Name

Website for Disability Support Resources

_____

_____

_____

Phone Number for Disability Support Resources

_____

_____

_____

Elder Care

Elder care refers to the support and assistance provided to older adults who may require help with their daily activities due to physical, cognitive, or medical conditions. Elder care can include a range of services, including:

- **In-home care:** This may involve a caregiver coming to the senior's home to provide assistance with daily tasks such as bathing, dressing, meal preparation, and medication management.

- **Assisted living facilities:** These are residential facilities that provide housing, meals, housekeeping, transportation, and assistance with daily activities.

- **Nursing homes:** These are long-term care facilities that provide 24-hour medical care and assistance with daily activities for seniors who require more extensive care.

- **Adult day care:** This involves seniors spending the day at a facility where they can participate in social activities, receive meals and snacks, and receive assistance with daily tasks.

- **Hospice care:** This is end-of-life care that focuses on providing comfort and support to individuals who are terminally ill and their families.

Elder care may also include legal and financial planning, transportation services, and other support services that can help seniors maintain their independence and quality of life.

Organization Name

_____

_____

Website for Elder Care Resources

_____

_____

Phone Number for Elder Care Resources

_____

_____

National Alliance on Mental Illness (NAMI)

The National Alliance on Mental Illness (NAMI) is an American advocacy group that provides support, education, and resources for individuals and families affected by mental illness. NAMI offers programs and services such as support groups, education classes, advocacy, and helplines to help those affected by mental illness better understand their conditions and cope with the challenges they may face. NAMI also works to raise awareness and reduce the stigma surrounding mental illness, and advocates for policies and funding to improve mental health care and services.

Organization Name

_____

_____

Website for Mental Health Resources

_____

_____

Phone Number for Mental Health Resources

_____

_____

_____

Legal Resources

Legal resources refer to organizations or entities that provide legal advice or assistance to individuals or businesses. They may offer free or low-cost legal services, advice, and information to help people understand their legal rights and responsibilities.

Some examples of legal resources include:

- **Legal aid organizations:** Nonprofit organizations that provide free or low-cost legal services to individuals and families who cannot afford an attorney. These organizations may specialize in certain areas of law, such as family law or immigration law.

- **Bar associations:** Organizations of licensed attorneys in a specific jurisdiction that provide legal resources, referrals, and support to both attorneys and the public.

- **Law clinics:** Law schools may operate clinics that provide legal services to the community under the supervision of law professors and licensed attorneys.

- **Self-help legal resources:** Online resources, books, and guides that provide information and guidance on legal issues for individuals who cannot afford or do not wish to hire an attorney.

- **Court-sponsored programs:** Some courts may offer programs such as legal assistance clinics or self-help centers to help individuals navigate the legal system and understand their rights.

- **Pro bono programs:** Many attorneys and law firms offer pro bono (free) legal services to individuals and organizations in need.

Chapter 7: IMPORTANT RESOURCES

Law Firm

Firm Name

Contact Information

Legal Aid Organization

Organization Name

Contact Information

Notes

Financial Resources

Financial resources are tools, services, and organizations that can provide assistance with managing finances, such as budgeting, saving, investing, and obtaining credit. These resources can be especially useful for individuals or families facing financial challenges or looking to improve their financial well-being. Here are some examples of financial resources:

- **Financial Counseling:** Financial counseling is a service provided by many organizations that can help individuals develop a budget, manage debt, and plan for their financial future.

- **Non-Profit Credit Counseling:** Non-profit credit counseling organizations can provide financial education, debt management plans, and credit counseling services to help individuals manage their debt.

- **Financial Education Resources:** Financial education resources can include books, websites, and classes that provide information and guidance on financial topics.

- **Financial Planning Services:** Financial planning services can help individuals plan for their financial future, such as retirement planning, estate planning, and investment management.

- **Government Programs:** Government programs, such as the Federal Trade Commission (FTC) and the Consumer Financial Protection Bureau (CFPB), provide information and resources to help consumers with financial issues, such as identity theft, credit reporting, and debt collection.

- **Community Organizations:** Community organizations, such as churches, non-profit organizations, and local government agencies, can offer financial assistance to individuals in need.

- **Online Tools:** There are many online tools available to help individuals with budgeting, saving, investing, and managing their finances. These tools include budgeting apps, financial calculators, and investment tracking software.

- **Credit Monitoring Services:** Credit monitoring services can help individuals keep track of their credit report and monitor for any changes or suspicious activity.

- **Loan Services:** Loan services, such as banks, credit unions, and online lenders, can provide individuals with loans for various purposes, such as purchasing a home, starting a business, or paying off debt.

- **Investment Services:** Investment services, such as brokerage firms and financial advisors, can provide individuals with guidance and advice on investing their money.

Debt Management

Organization Name

Contact Information

Notes

Financial Assistance Program

Program Name

Contact Information

Notes

Community Resources

Community resources refer to various local organizations, agencies, and services that provide assistance to people in need. These resources can include food banks, homeless shelters, community centers, and public libraries, among others.

Food banks are a type of community resource that provides food assistance to people who are struggling with hunger. These organizations often rely on donations from individuals and businesses to provide food to those in need. Homeless shelters, on the other hand, provide temporary housing and support services to people who are experiencing homelessness. Community centers are places where people can gather for social and recreational activities, as well as educational and wellness programs. Public libraries are another valuable community resource that provide access to books, computers, and other educational resources.

In addition to these examples, there are many other community resources available that can help people in various ways. Some communities have organizations that provide legal assistance, job training programs, transportation services, and other types of support. These resources can be especially important for individuals and families who are facing financial or other challenges. It's always a good idea to research and familiarize yourself with the community resources available in your area so that you can access them if needed.

Local Support Group

_____

_____

_____

Group Name

_____

_____

_____

Contact Information

_____

_____

_____

Community Center

_____

_____

_____

Center Name

Contact Information

Notes

Emergency Resources

Emergency resources refer to the organizations, services, and individuals that provide immediate assistance in case of a crisis, disaster, or emergency situation. These resources include:

- **Emergency medical services (EMS):** EMS personnel respond to medical emergencies and provide life-saving interventions, such as CPR, defibrillation, and administering medications.

- **Fire and rescue services:** Firefighters and rescue workers respond to fires, accidents, and other emergencies, providing fire suppression, rescue, and other assistance.

- **Law enforcement agencies:** Law enforcement agencies such as police departments, sheriff's offices, and state troopers respond to emergencies involving criminal activity or public safety.

- **Disaster relief organizations:** Organizations such as the American Red Cross, Salvation Army, and FEMA provide aid to people affected by natural disasters such as hurricanes, floods, and earthquakes.

- **Emergency shelters:** Shelters provide a safe place to stay for people who are displaced due to disasters, homelessness, or other emergencies.

- **Poison control centers:** Poison control centers provide advice and assistance in case of poisoning emergencies.

- **Crisis hotlines:** Crisis hotlines provide confidential support and assistance to people in crisis, including suicide prevention and mental health services.

- **Utility companies:** Utility companies such as electricity, gas, and water providers have emergency response teams that can quickly restore service in case of outages or other emergencies.

It's important to have a list of emergency resources and their contact information readily available in case of an emergency.

Emergency Services

Service Name

Contact Information

Disaster Relief Organization

Organization Name

Contact Information

Shelter

Shelter refers to a place where someone can live, usually on a temporary basis, when they have nowhere else to go or cannot stay in their current home. Shelters can be run by government agencies, non-profit organizations, or other groups, and can offer a variety of services such as meals, clothing, and counseling in addition to housing. Shelters can provide temporary housing for people experiencing homelessness, victims of domestic violence or other crises, and people displaced by natural disasters or other emergencies. Some shelters may have specific requirements for entry, such as sobriety, while others may be open to anyone in need.

Shelter Name

Contact Information

Chapter 8:

TO-DO LIST

———

The "To-Do List" section serves as a reminder to gather and organize important documents and records. These documents are essential for various purposes, such as identification, legal matters, financial planning, and estate management. Here's a breakdown of the list of documents and their possible locations:

List of Documents Needed:

- **Passport:** A travel document used for international travel and identification.

- **Driver's License:** A government-issued identification card for driving privileges.

- **Social Security Card:** An official document containing your unique Social Security number.

- **Birth Certificate:** A document that provides proof of your birth and identity.

- **Marriage Certificate:** A legal document that verifies a marriage between two individuals.

- **Divorce Decree:** A legal document that outlines the terms of a divorce settlement.

- **Will:** A legal document that outlines how your assets will be distributed after your death.

- **Trust:** A legal arrangement where a trustee manages assets on behalf of beneficiaries.

- **Power of Attorney:** A legal document that authorizes someone to act on your behalf in legal and financial matters.

- **Health Care Directives:** Legal documents that outline your wishes for medical treatment and end-of-life care.

- **Insurance Policies:** Documents related to life, health, auto, home, or other insurance coverage.

- **Retirement Account Information:** Documents related to your retirement accounts, such as 401(k) or IRA statements.

- **Investment Account Information:** Documents related to your investment accounts, such as brokerage or mutual fund statements.

- **Bank Account Information:** Details about your bank accounts, including account numbers and contact information.

- **Credit Card Information:** Details about your credit cards, including account numbers and contact information.

- **Tax Returns:** Copies of your tax returns for the last three years.

- **Property Deeds and Titles:** Documents that prove ownership of real estate or other properties.

- **Vehicle Registration:** Documents related to the registration and ownership of your vehicles.

- **Military Records (If Applicable):** Documents related to your military service, such as discharge papers or service records.

Location of Documents:

- **Home Safe or Lockbox:** Keep important documents in a secure safe or lockbox at your residence.

- **Bank Safety Deposit Box:** Rent a safety deposit box at a bank to store important documents.

- **Trusted Friend or Family Member's Home:** Entrust a close friend or family member with copies of important documents.

- **Lawyer's Office:** Store copies of legal documents at your lawyer's office for safekeeping.

- **Other:** Specify any other locations where you may have stored copies of important documents, such as a digital cloud storage service or a trusted advisor's office.

Remember to keep the originals and copies of these documents in a secure and easily accessible place, and inform trusted individuals about their location in case of emergencies or when they are needed.

Set Aside Time to Fill out Each Section of the Journal:

Date: _____

Time: _____

- Discuss and Make Decisions with Partner on Important Topics

Date of Discussion: _____

Topics Discussed: _____

_____

_____

_____

_____

_____

- Update as Needed with Changes in Personal Information or Circumstances

Date of Update: _____

Information Updated: _____

_____

_____

_____

_____

_____

- Keep in a Safe and Easily Accessible Location

Location: _____

_____

_____

- Periodically Review and Update Information as Necessary

Date of Review: _____

Information Updated: _____

_____

_____

- Inform Trusted Loved Ones or Executor of the Existence and Location of the Journal

Name of Individual Informed: _____

Relationship to Couple: _____

Name of Individual Informed: _____

Relationship to Couple: _____

Name of Individual Informed: _____

Relationship to Couple: _____

Name of Individual Informed: _____

Relationship to Couple: _____

Name of Individual Informed: _____

Relationship to Couple: _____

Name of Individual Informed: _____

Relationship to Couple: _____

Name of Individual Informed: _____

Chapter 9:

THOUGHTS & FINAL WISHES

———

T he "Thoughts & Final Wishes" section provides an opportunity for you to express your personal thoughts, reflections, and final wishes for the future. It allows you to share your desires, beliefs, and values with your loved ones and those responsible for carrying out your wishes after you're gone. Here are some key aspects to consider:

- **Personal Thoughts:** This section can include any personal reflections, messages, or sentiments you want to convey to your loved ones. It may include messages of love, gratitude, or advice that you want to leave behind.

- **Inspirations:** You can share your sources of inspiration, such as quotes, poems, or books that have influenced you. These can serve as guidance and inspiration for your family and friends.

- **Final Wishes:** This section is an opportunity to express your wishes for your funeral or memorial service. You can specify whether you prefer a burial or cremation, the type of ceremony you would like, and any specific requests regarding music, readings, or rituals.

- **Legacy and Charitable Contributions:** If you have specific wishes for how you want to be remembered or if you want to make charitable contributions in your name, you can include those details here. This can involve specifying organizations or causes that are meaningful to you.

- **Digital Assets and Online Presence:** With the increasing digital presence in our lives, you may want to address your digital assets, such as social media accounts, email accounts, and digital files. You can provide instructions on how you want these assets to be handled or if you want them to be preserved or deleted.

It's important to regularly review and update this section to ensure your thoughts and wishes accurately reflect your current mindset and intentions. Consider discussing these matters with your loved ones, legal advisors, or estate planners to ensure that your wishes are known and can be properly carried out when the time comes.

This section is for you to record any personal thoughts, inspirations, and wishes for the future. It's an opportunity to reflect on your life together and document your aspirations for the years to come.

Here are Some Prompts to get Started:

Type of Service Desired

Religious: _____

Secular: _____

Other: _____

Burial or Cremation

Burial: _____

Cremation: _____

Cemetery or

Final Resting Place: _____

Phone: _____

eMail: _____

Relationship: _____

Other Important Details: _____

Special Requests or Traditions

Music: _____

Readings: _____

Poems: _____

Flowers: _____

Charitiable Donations: _____

Other: _____

Preferred Funeral Home: _____

Contact Information: _____

Name: _____

Address: _____

City: _____

State: _____   Zip Code: _____

Country: _____

Phone: _____

eMail: _____

Notes: _____

End of Life Care

Preferred Medical Facility: _____

Facility Contact Information: _____

Advanced Directive: _____

Living Will: _____

Do Not Resuscitate

(DNR) Orders: _____

Hospice or Palliative

Care Preferences: _____

Other Important Details: _____

Memorial Service or Celebration of Life Preferences

Preferred Date: _____

Preferred Time: _____

Theme or Tone of Service: _____

Music to be Included: _____

Readings to be Included: _____

Special Requests or
Traditions: _____

Other Important Details: _____

Preferred Obituary Information

Name: _____

Age: _____

Residence at Time of
Passing: _____

Date of Death: _____

Cause of Death: _____

Surviving Family: _____

Preferred Charities: _____

Special Accomplishments
Or Achievements: _____

Charitable Organizations to be Notified

Name of Organization: _____

Contact Information: _____

Preferred Donation Type: _____

Preferred Donation Amount: _____

Name of Organization: _____

Contact Information: _____

Preferred Donation Type: _____

Preferred Donation Amount: _____

Personal Items to be Distributed or Passed Down

The section on "Personal Items to be Distributed or Passed Down" allows you to specify the personal belongings that you wish to distribute among your loved ones or pass down as heirlooms. These items hold sentimental value and can carry memories and stories that you want to preserve within your family. Here are some considerations for this section:

- **List of Items:** Create a detailed list of personal items that you want to distribute or pass down. These items can include jewelry, artwork, furniture, family heirlooms, photographs, sentimental objects, collections, or any other possessions that hold personal significance to you.

- **Recipients:** Indicate the names of the individuals whom you wish to receive each specific item. This can include family members, friends, or other loved ones. Be as specific as possible to avoid confusion or potential disputes.

- **Instructions:** If you have any specific instructions or wishes regarding the distribution or preservation of certain items, make sure to include them. For example, you may want to specify that a particular piece of jewelry should be given to a specific family member on a special occasion, or that a certain artwork should be displayed in a particular location.

141

- **Legacy Letters:** Consider writing personal letters to accompany certain items. These letters can explain the significance of the item, share memories associated with it, or express your hopes for its future preservation. This can provide a deeper understanding and connection to the item for the recipient.

- **Executor or Trustee:** If you have designated an executor or trustee to handle your estate, ensure that they are aware of your wishes regarding the distribution of personal items. Provide them with a copy of this section to ensure that your instructions are followed.

Remember to periodically review and update this section as your preferences may change over time. Open communication with your loved ones about your intentions and the significance of these items can also help to ensure a smooth and respectful distribution process.

List of Items to be Given and Who They Should be Given to:

_____

_____

_____

_____

_____

Instructions on How to Distribute Items:

_____

_____

_____

_____

Special Requests or Conditions for Certain Items:

_____

_____

Other Final Wishes or Instructions:

_____

_____

_____

PART 2:
EXPLANATION
(PERSON 2)

As a husband and/or wife/ or partner, it's important to keep track of your person al information in one place and maybe even property/properties you both own. In this section, you'll combine your information in the following subsections:

In this section, Partner 1 will fill out the following ten subsections:

Personal Information

Personal information refers to any information that can be used to identify an individual. The name, address, phone number, email, social security number, date of birth, emergency contact information, employment history, and education history are all examples of personal information.

- **Name:** This is the name that a person goes by, which could include their first name, middle name, and last name. It's used to identify the individual.

- **Address:** This refers to the location where the individual resides or can be reached, such as a home or office address.

- **Phone number:** This is a set of digits used to contact the individual via phone call or text message.

- **Email:** This is an electronic address used to communicate with the individual online.

- **Social security number:** This is a unique nine-digit number issued by the government that identifies individuals for tax and social security purposes.

- **Date of birth:** This refers to the day, month, and year that an individual was born and is used to confirm their identity.

- **Emergency contact information:** This is the name, phone number, and relationship of a person to be contacted in case of an emergency.

- **Employment history:** This includes information about an individual's work experience, such as their job titles, employers, and dates of employment.

- **Education history:** This includes information about an individual's educational background, such as the name of schools attended, degrees earned, and graduation dates.

It's important to protect personal information as it can be used for identity theft, fraud, or other malicious purposes. Organizations that collect and store personal information have a responsibility to keep it safe and secure, and individuals should also take measures to protect their personal information, such as using strong passwords and being cautious about sharing it online.

Important Contacts

Important contacts refer to the individuals who should be notified or contacted in the event of an emergency, or those who are crucial to Person 2's daily life. These could include family members, friends, neighbors, or other individuals who have a close relationship with Person 2.

When listing important contacts, it's important to include the person's full name, phone number, email address, and their relationship to Person 2. This information can be used to quickly and easily contact these individuals in case of an emergency or if Person 1 needs assistance.

Family members are often the first individuals to be listed as important contacts, as they are typically the closest and most trusted people in one's life. This could include parents, siblings, children, or other relatives.

Friends and neighbors could also be important contacts, especially if Person 2 is not in contact with family members or lives far away from them. In case of an emergency or need for assistance, these individuals could help provide support or resources.

It's also important to consider any other individuals who play an important role in Person 2's life, such as a doctor, lawyer, or financial advisor. These individuals can provide important guidance and support in times of need.

Listing and regularly updating important contacts can be helpful in ensuring that Person 2 has a support system in place and that their loved ones are informed and able to help in case of an emergency.

Financial Information

Financial information refers to any information related to a person's financial situation, including their income, expenses, debts, assets, and investments. The financial information that may be important to include in a document could include:

- **Bank accounts:** This refers to any accounts held with financial institutions, such as checking accounts, savings accounts, or money market accounts.

- **Credit cards:** This refers to any credit cards that Person 2 may have, including the issuer, account number, and payment due dates.

- **Loans:** This refers to any outstanding loans that Person 2 may have, including mortgages, car loans, or personal loans. It's important to include the name of the lender, the amount owed, and the payment due date.

- **Investments:** This refers to any investments that Person 2 may have, such as stocks, bonds, mutual funds, or retirement accounts. It's important to include the name of the investment, the account number, and the institution where it's held.

- **Insurance policies:** This refers to any insurance policies that Person 2 may have, such as life insurance, health insurance, or auto insurance. It's important to include the name of the insurance company, the policy number, and the contact information for the agent or representative.

- **Taxes:** This refers to any information related to Person 2's tax situation, such as their tax ID number, past tax returns, and any outstanding tax debts.

- **Cryptocurrency and Bitcoin accounts:** This refers to any digital currency holdings, including Bitcoin and other cryptocurrencies. It's important to include the name of the cryptocurrency, the account number, and the platform where it's held.

Including this financial information in a document can be helpful for loved ones in the event of an emergency or if Person 1 is unable to manage their finances. It can also help with estate planning and ensuring that assets are distributed according to Person 2's wishes. However, it's important to keep this information secure and to only share it with trusted individuals.

Real Estate and Property

Real estate and property refer to any physical assets that Person 2 owns, including their home, rental properties, vehicles, land, and any other assets of value. When documenting real estate and property, it's important to include the following details:

- **Value:** This refers to the estimated value of the property or asset. This can be determined through appraisals or market research.

- **Location:** This refers to the physical address of the property or asset.

- **Ownership details:** This refers to the legal ownership of the property or asset, including any liens or mortgages that may be attached to it.

For homes and rental properties, it's important to include the name of the mortgage lender, the loan number, and the contact information for the lender. For vehicles, it's important to include the make, model, and year of the vehicle, as well as the vehicle identification number (VIN).

In the case of land, it's important to include the location of the land, the legal description of the property, and any survey information. It may also be helpful to include any zoning or land use restrictions that may apply to the property.

By documenting real estate and property, Person 2 can ensure that their loved ones are aware of their assets and that they are distributed according to their wishes in the event of their death or incapacity. It can also help with estate planning and tax planning. However, it's important to keep this information secure and to only share it with trusted individuals.

Monthly Bills and Subscriptions

Monthly bills and subscriptions refer to any recurring expenses that Person 2 may have, including bills for utilities, rent/mortgage payments, subscriptions for magazines, streaming services, gym memberships, and any other monthly payments.

When documenting monthly bills and subscriptions, it's important to include the following details:

- **Due dates:** This refers to the date on which the bill or subscription payment is due.

- **Amounts:** This refers to the cost of the bill or subscription.

- **Payment methods:** This refers to the method that Person 2 uses to pay the bill or subscription, such as automatic bank transfers or credit card payments.

Having a record of monthly bills and subscriptions can be helpful for both Person 2 and their loved ones. It can help Person 2 keep track of their expenses and ensure that bills are paid on time. In the event that Person 2 is unable to manage their finances, having a record of their bills and subscriptions can help loved ones ensure that these payments are still being made on time.

It's also important to regularly review and update this information, as monthly bills and subscriptions can change over time. By keeping this information up to date, Person 2 can ensure that their loved ones have access to the most current information in case of an emergency.

Health and Medical Information

Health and medical information refers to any information related to Person 2's medical history, current medical conditions, allergies, medications, and doctors they may be seeing. When documenting health and medical information, it's important to include the following details:

- **Medical history:** This refers to any previous medical conditions or surgeries that Person 1 has had.

- **Current medical conditions:** This refers to any ongoing medical conditions that Person 2 is currently managing.

- **Allergies:** This refers to any allergies that Person 2 may have to medications, food, or other substances.

- **Medications:** This refers to any medications that Person 2 is currently taking, including dosage and frequency.

- **Doctors:** This refers to any doctors or healthcare providers that Person 2 is seeing, including their names, specialties, and contact information.

Having a record of health and medical information can be critical in the event of an emergency. It can help medical professionals make informed decisions about Person 2's care, especially if they are unable to communicate or if their loved ones are not present to provide this information. It can also be helpful for personal health management, ensuring that Person 2 is aware of their own medical history and any ongoing conditions they may be managing.

However, it's important to keep this information private and secure, and to only share it with trusted individuals such as healthcare providers or designated emergency contacts.

Legal Documents

Legal documents refer to any documents that have legal significance, such as a will, power of attorney, living will, prenuptial agreement, cohabitation agreement, or any other legal documents that Person 2 may have. When documenting legal documents, it's important to include the following details:

- **Location:** This refers to where the original documents are stored, such as a safe deposit box, lawyer's office, or home safe.

- **Contact information:** This refers to the contact information for any lawyers or legal professionals involved in drafting or executing the documents, as well as any individuals named in the documents, such as an executor or power of attorney.

Having a record of legal documents can be critical in ensuring that Person 2's wishes are carried out in the event of their death or incapacity. It can also be helpful for personal legal management, ensuring that Person 2 is aware of their legal rights and obligations. It's important to keep these documents private and secure, and to only share them with trusted individuals such as lawyers or designated emergency contacts. Additionally, it's important to regularly review and update these documents as circumstances may change over time, such as changes in family relationships, health status, or financial situations.

Passwords and Online Accounts

Passwords and online accounts refer to any usernames and passwords that Person 2 may use for online accounts, websites, and other digital services, as well as any passwords for electronic devices, safes, or safety deposit boxes. When documenting passwords and online accounts, it's important to include the following details:

- **Username:** This refers to the username or account name associated with the online account or digital service.

- **Password:** This refers to the password associated with the username or account name.

- **Website or service:** This refers to the website or digital service associated with the username and password.

Having a record of passwords and online accounts can be helpful for both personal use and emergency situations. It can help Person 2 keep track of their accounts and ensure that they are able to access them when needed. In the event that Person 2 is unable to manage their accounts, having a record of their passwords and accounts can help loved ones access important information or accounts on their behalf.

However, it's important to keep this information private and secure, and to only share it with trusted individuals such as designated emergency contacts. It's also important to regularly update passwords and review account activity to ensure that they remain secure and protected against any potential security breaches.

Thoughts and Wishes

Thoughts and wishes refer to any personal reflections, aspirations, or goals that Person 2 may have for their future. When documenting thoughts and wishes, it's important to include the following details:

- **Personal thoughts:** This refers to any personal reflections or musings that Person 2 may have, such as memories, experiences, or personal philosophies.

- **Inspirations:** This refers to any sources of inspiration that Person 2 may have, such as books, music, or art.

- **Wishes for the future:** This refers to any aspirations or goals that Person 2 may have for their future, such as travel plans, career goals, or personal milestones.

Having a record of thoughts and wishes can be helpful for personal reflection and goal-setting, as well as for loved ones who may want to understand Person 2's perspectives or values. It can also provide comfort in the event of Person 2's passing, as loved ones may be able to honor their wishes or reflect on their personal thoughts.

However, it's important to ensure that thoughts and wishes are kept private and secure, and that they are only shared with trusted individuals or designated emergency contacts. Additionally, it's important to regularly review and update thoughts and wishes as circumstances or goals may change over time.

Medications To-Go Page

The Medications To-Go page is a document that contains a list of Person 2's medications and dosages, which can be used in emergency situations. When documenting medications to-go, it's important to include the following details:

- **Medication name:** This refers to the name of the medication that Person 2 is taking.

- **Dosage:** This refers to the amount of medication that Person 2 is taking, as well as how often it should be taken.

- **Route of administration:** This refers to how the medication should be taken, such as orally, through injection, or topically.

Having a list of medications and dosages can be critical in emergency situations, especially if Person 2 is unable to communicate their medical history or current medications. The Medications To-Go page can be kept in a convenient location such as a wallet or purse, and can be used to quickly provide information to emergency responders or medical professionals.

However, it's important to ensure that the Medications To-Go page is regularly updated and that any changes to medications or dosages are reflected on the document. It's also important to consult with a healthcare provider before making any changes to medication regimens or dosages.

PART 2:
INDIVIDUAL INFORMATION (Person 2)

Individual Information refers to the personal details and background information about Person 2. This information can be important for both personal reference and emergency situations. When documenting Individual Information, it's important to include the following details:

- **Full name:** This refers to the legal name of Person 2.

- **Address:** This refers to the current physical address of Person 2, as well as any other relevant addresses (such as previous addresses or vacation homes).

- **Phone number:** This refers to the primary phone number where Person 2 can be reached.

- **Email address:** This refers to the primary email address where Person 2 can be reached.

- **Social Security number:** This refers to Person 2's unique nine-digit Social Security number, which is used for tax and other government-related purposes.

- **Date of birth:** This refers to Person 2's date of birth.

- **Emergency contact information:** This refers to the name, phone number, and relationship of the person who should be contacted in case of an emergency.

- **Employment history:** This refers to Person 2's previous and current employment, including job titles, employers, and dates of employment.

- **Education history:** This refers to Person 2's educational background, including degrees, institutions attended, and dates of attendance.

Having a record of Individual Information can be helpful for personal reference and in emergency situations where this information may be needed quickly. However, it's important to ensure that this information is kept private and secure, and that it is only shared with trusted individuals or designated emergency contacts. Additionally, it's important to regularly review and update Individual Information as circumstances may change over time.

Husband/Wife/Life Partner 2:

Personal information for Husband/Wife/Life Partner 2 refers to the personal details and background information about the person's spouse or partner. When documenting Personal Information for Husband/Wife/Life Partner 2, it's important to include the following details.

- **Full name**: This refers to the legal name of the person's spouse or partner.

- **Date of birth:** This refers to the date of birth of the person's spouse or partner.

- **Contact information:** This includes the phone number, email address, and physical address of the person's spouse or partner.

- **Social Security number:** This refers to the unique nine-digit Social Security number of the person's spouse or partner, which is used for tax and other government-related purposes.

- **Employment history:** This includes the previous and current employment history of the person's spouse or partner, including job titles, employers, and dates of employment.

- **Education history:** This includes the educational background of the person's spouse or partner, including degrees, institutions attended, and dates of attendance.

Having a record of Personal Information for Husband/Wife/Life Partner 2 can be helpful for personal reference and in emergency situations where this information may be needed quickly. However, it's important to ensure that this information is kept private and secure, and that it is only shared with trusted individuals or designated emergency contacts. Additionally, it's important to regularly review and update this information as circumstances may change over time.

Personal Information:

Full Name: _____

Address: _____

City: _____

State: _____ Zip Code: _____

Country: _____

Home: _____

Mobile: _____

Work: _____

Home eMail: _____

Date of Birth: _____

Social Security Number: _____

In this section, the first partner will fill out the following ten subsections:

Emergency Contact Information:

Emergency Contact Information refers to the names, phone numbers, and relationships of the people who should be contacted in case of an emergency. When documenting Emergency Contact Information, it's important to include the following details:

- **Name:** This refers to the full name of the emergency contact.

- **Phone number:** This refers to the primary phone number where the emergency contact can be reached.

- **Email address:** This refers to the primary email address where the emergency contact can be reached.

- **Relationship:** This refers to the relationship of the emergency contact to the person who is creating the document. Examples of relationships can include spouse, child, parent, sibling, friend, neighbor, or colleague.

Having a record of Emergency Contact Information can be extremely helpful in case of an emergency, such as a sudden illness, injury, or accident. By having this information readily available, emergency responders and medical professionals can quickly contact the appropriate people and provide important updates about the person's condition. It's important to keep this information up-to-date and to inform the emergency contacts that they have been designated as such.

Person 1

Full Name: _____

Address: _____

City: _____

State: _____ Zip Code: _____

Country: _____

Home: _____

Mobile: _____

Work: _____

Home eMail: _____

Date of Birth: _____

Social Security Number: _____

Phone: _____

eMail: _____

Relationship: _____

Other Important Details: _____

_____

_____

Emergency Contact Information (Person 2)

Emergency Contact Information for Person 2 refers to the names, phone numbers, and relationships of the people who should be contacted in case of an emergency for Person 2. When documenting Emergency Contact Information for Person 2, it's important to include the following details:

- **Name:** This refers to the full name of the emergency contact for Person 2.

- **Phone number:** This refers to the primary phone number where the emergency contact can be reached in case of an emergency related to Person 2.

- **Email address:** This refers to the primary email address where the emergency contact can be reached in case of an emergency related to Person 2.

- **Relationship:** This refers to the relationship of the emergency contact to Person 2. Examples of relationships can include spouse, child, parent, sibling, friend, neighbor, or colleague.

In some cases, it may also be useful to include additional information about the emergency contact, such as their address, workplace, or any other relevant details that may be needed in an emergency situation.

Having Emergency Contact Information for Person 2 can be crucial in case of an emergency, such as a sudden illness, injury, or accident that renders Person 2 unable to communicate or make decisions. By having this information readily available, emergency responders and medical professionals can quickly contact the appropriate people and provide important updates about Person 2's condition. It's important to keep this information up-to-date and to inform the emergency contacts that they have been designated as such.

Person 2

Full Name: _____
Address: _____
City: _____
State: _____ Zip Code: _____
Country: _____
Home: _____
Mobile: _____
Work: _____
Home eMail: _____
Date of Birth: _____
Social Security Number: _____
Phone: _____
eMail: _____
Relationship: _____
Other Important Details: _____

_____

Employment

Employment information for Person 2 refers to the details of their current or previous employment. When documenting Employment Information for Person 2, it's important to include the following details:

- **Employer name:** This refers to the name of Person 2's current or previous employer.

- **Job title:** This refers to the job title of Person 1's current or previous role.

- **Start and end date:** This refers to the start and end date of Person 2's employment in that role.

- **Salary:** This refers to the salary or hourly wage that Person 2 received for their work.

- **Contact information:** This refers to the contact information of the employer, including the address, phone number, and email address.

Additionally, it may also be useful to include information about any benefits or retirement plans that Person 2 is enrolled in, as well as any relevant human resources contact information.

Having accurate Employment Information for Person 2 can be important for a number of reasons, such as when applying for loans or other financial services, or for tax purposes. It can also be helpful to have this information readily available in case of an emergency, such as if Person 2 is suddenly unable to work due to illness or injury.

Employer Name: _____

Job Title: _____

Work Address: _____

Work Phone: _____

Date of Hire: _____ Annual Salary: _____

Education History

Education history refers to the academic and educational background of a person, which includes information on their degrees, diplomas, and certifications. When documenting Education History, it is important to include the following details:

- **Institution Name:** This refers to the name of the educational institution where the person studied.

- **Degree/Certificate:** This refers to the type of degree or certificate that the person earned, such as a Bachelor's degree, Master's degree, or a professional certification.

- **Major/Area of Study:** This refers to the subject or field that the person specialized in while pursuing their degree or certificate.

- **Dates Attended:** This refers to the duration of time that the person was enrolled in the educational institution.

- **Honors/ Awards:** This refers to any honors or awards received by the person during their academic journey, such as a summa cum laude or magna cum laude distinction.

It may also be useful to include any additional information such as the location of the educational institution, the name of the program or department, and the contact information of the school's registrar office.

Having accurate Education History information for a person is important in a number of scenarios, such as job applications, further education pursuits, or even for personal records. It can also be helpful to have this information readily available in case of an emergency, such as if a person requires medical treatment and the healthcare provider needs to know their educational background.

Highest Degree Earned: _____

Institution Name: _____

Field of Study: _____

Degree Type: _____ Graduation Date: _____

Family Information

Family information refers to the details of the family members of a person, such as their spouse, children, parents, and siblings. When documenting Family Information, it is important to include the following details:

- **Name:** This refers to the name of each family member, including their first and last name.

- **Relationship:** This refers to the relationship of the family member to the person, such as spouse, parent, child, or sibliwng.

- **Date of Birth:** This refers to the date of birth of each family member.

- **Contact Information:** This refers to the contact information of each family member, including their phone number, email address, and physical address.

Additionally, it may also be useful to include information about any important events related to family members, such as weddings, births, or deaths.

Having accurate Family Information for a person can be important for a number of reasons, such as when planning family events or reunions, or for medical reasons such as in case of genetic disorders or family medical history. It can also be helpful to have this information readily available in case of an emergency, such as if a family member needs to be contacted quickly.

The subsections for this section can include:

Details for family members

Spouse

A spouse refers to a person's husband or wife, in a legally recognized marriage. When documenting information about a spouse, it is important to include the following details:

- **Personal Information:** This includes the spouse's full name, date of birth, place of birth, and contact information such as phone number, email address, and physical address.

- **Marriage Information:** This includes the date and location of the marriage, as well as any other details relevant to the marriage, such as whether it was a civil or religious ceremony.

- **Employment Information:** This includes the spouse's employment history, including their current employer, job title, and length of employment.

- **Education Information:** This includes the spouse's education history, including the schools they attended, degrees earned, and areas of study.

- **Family Information:** This includes details about the spouse's family members, such as their parents and siblings, including their names, dates of birth, and contact information.

Having accurate information about a spouse is important for a number of reasons, such as for legal and financial matters, healthcare decisions, and emergency situations. It is also important to keep this information up to date in case of any changes, such as a change of address or employment.

Full Name: _____

Address: _____

City: _____

State: _____ Zip Code: _____

Country: _____

Home: _____

Mobile: _____

Work: _____

Home eMail: _____

Date of Birth: _____

Social Security Number: _____

Spouse's Employment

When documenting a spouse's employment information, it is important to include details such as:

- **Current Employer:** This includes the name of the spouse's current employer.

- **Job Title:** This refers to the title or position held by the spouse in their current job.

- **Date of Employment:** This refers to the date the spouse started working with their current employer.

- **Work Contact Information:** This includes the phone number, email address, and physical address of the spouse's workplace.

- **Work History:** This includes the spouse's work history, such as previous employers, job titles, and dates of employment.

Having accurate employment information for a spouse can be important for a number of reasons, such as for tax purposes, loan applications, or in the event of an emergency. It can also be useful to keep this information up to date in case of any changes, such as a change in job or employer.

Employer Name: _____

Job Title: _____

Work Address: _____

Work Phone: _____

Date of Hire: _____ Annual Salary: _____

Spouse's Education History

When documenting a spouse's education history, it is important to include details such as:

- **Schools Attended:** This includes the names of the schools the spouse attended, including the name of the institution and the name of the degree program.

- **Degree(s) Earned:** This includes the type of degree(s) the spouse earned, such as a Bachelor's, Master's, or Doctorate degree.

- **Area(s) of Study:** This includes the subject area or field of study the spouse pursued, such as business, engineering, or education.

- **Dates of Attendance:** This includes the dates when the spouse attended each school, including the start and end dates.

Having accurate education information for a spouse can be important for a number of reasons, such as for job applications, educational opportunities, or in the event of an emergency. It can also be useful to keep this information up to date in case of any changes, such as completing a new degree program or pursuing further education.

Highest Degree Earned: _____

Institution Name: _____

Field of Study: _____

Degree Type: _____ Graduation Date: _____

Children

When documenting information about children, it is important to include details such as:

- **Full Name:** This includes the full name of each child.

- **Date of Birth:** This refers to the date of birth of each child.

- **Relationship:** This indicates the relationship of each child to the person or couple documenting the information, such as "biological child," "adopted child," "stepchild," etc.

- **Contact Information:** This includes the phone number, email address, and physical address of each child.

- **School Information:** This includes the name and address of the school each child attends, as well as their grade level.

- **Medical Information:** This includes any relevant medical information about each child, such as allergies or chronic conditions.

Having accurate information about children can be important for a number of reasons, such as for medical emergencies, school activities, or in the event of a legal dispute. It can also be useful to keep this information up to date in case of any changes, such as a change in school or medical condition.

• First Child

Full Name: _____

Address: _____

City: _____

State: _____ Zip Code: _____

Country: _____

Phone: _____

eMail: _____

Date of Birth: _____

Social Security Number: _____

Education: _____

• Second Child

Full Name: _____

Address: _____

City: _____

State: _____ Zip Code: _____

Country: _____

Phone: _____

eMail: _____

Date of Birth: _____

Social Security Number: _____

Education: _____

• Third Child

Full Name: _____

Address: _____

City: _____

State: _____ Zip Code: _____

Country: _____

Phone: _____

eMail: _____

Date of Birth: _____

Social Security Number: _____

Education: _____

• Fourth Child

Full Name: _____

Address: _____

City: _____

State: _____ Zip Code: _____

Country: _____

Phone: _____

eMail: _____

Date of Birth: _____

Social Security Number: _____

Education: _____

Parents

When documenting information about parents, it is important to include details such as:

• **Full Name:** This includes the full name of each parent.

- **Date of Birth:** This refers to the date of birth of each parent.

- **Contact Information:** This includes the phone number, email address, and physical address of each parent.

- **Medical Information:** This includes any relevant medical information about each parent, such as allergies or chronic conditions.

- **Employment Information:** This includes information about each parent's employment, such as their job title, company name, and contact information.

- **Education History:** This includes information about each parent's education history, such as the schools they attended and the degrees they earned.

Having accurate information about parents can be important for a number of reasons, such as for medical emergencies, family history research, or in the event of a legal dispute. It can also be useful to keep this information up to date in case of any changes, such as a change in contact information or medical condition.

• Father

Full Name: _____

Address: _____

City: _____

State: _____ Zip Code: _____

Country: _____

Phone: _____

eMail: _____

Date of Birth: _____

Social Security Number: _____

Education: _____

Other Important Details: _____

• Mother

Full Name: _____

Address: _____

City: _____

State: _____ Zip Code: _____

Country: _____

Phone: _____

eMail: _____

Date of Birth: _____

Social Security Number: _____

Education: _____

Other Important Details: _____

• Siblings

Full Name: _____

Address: _____

City: _____

State: _____ Zip Code: _____

Country: _____

Phone: _____

eMail: _____

Date of Birth: _____

Social Security Number: _____

Education: _____

Other Important Details: _____

• Siblings

Full Name: _____

Address: _____

City: _____

State: _____ Zip Code: _____

Country: _____

Phone: _____

eMail: _____

Date of Birth: _____

Social Security Number: _____

Education: _____

Other Important Details: _____

• Siblings

Full Name: _____

Address: _____

City: _____

State: _____ Zip Code: _____

Country: _____

Phone: _____

eMail: _____

Date of Birth: _____

Social Security Number: _____

Education: _____

Other Important Details: _____

Other Family Members:

When documenting information about other family members, it is important to include details such as:

- **Full Name:** This includes the full name of each family member.

- **Date of Birth:** This refers to the date of birth of each family member.

- **Relationship:** This indicates the relationship of each family member to the person or couple documenting the information, such as "sibling," "grandparent," "cousin," etc.

- **Contact Information:** This includes the phone number, email address, and physical address of each family member.

- **Medical Information:** This includes any relevant medical information about each family member, such as allergies or chronic conditions.

- **Employment Information:** This includes information about each family member's employment, such as their job title, company name, and contact information.

- **Education History:** This includes information about each family member's education history, such as the schools they attended and the degrees they earned.

Having accurate information about other family members can be important for a number of reasons, such as for medical emergencies, family history research, or in the event of a legal dispute. It can also be useful to keep this information up to date in case of any changes, such as a change in contact information or medical condition.

Full Name: _____

Address: _____

City: _____

State: _____ Zip Code: _____

Country: _____

Phone: _____

eMail: _____

Relationship: _____

Other Important Details: _____

_____

_____

Full Name: _____

Address: _____

City: _____

State: _____ Zip Code: _____

Country: _____

Phone: _____

eMail: _____

Relationship: _____

Other Important Details: _____

_____

_____

Chapter 10:

FINANCIAL INFORMATION

Financial information is an important part of any personal information document. Here are some details that can be included under this section:

- **Bank Accounts:** This includes details of all bank accounts held by the person, including the name of the bank, account number, account type (savings or checking), and the current balance.

- **Credit Cards:** This includes a list of all credit cards held by the person, including the name of the card issuer, card number, and the current balance.

- **Loans:** This includes details of any loans taken out by the person, including the name of the lender, the loan amount, and the current balance.

- **Investments:** This includes details of any investments made by the person, including the name of the investment, the amount invested, and the current value.

- **Insurance Policies:** This includes details of all insurance policies held by the person, including life insurance, health insurance, car insurance, and home insurance.

- **Taxes:** This includes details of the person's tax status, including their tax ID number, filing status, and any outstanding tax payments.

- **Cryptocurrency:** This includes information about any cryptocurrency owned by the person, such as Bitcoin or Ethereum, including the amount owned and any associated wallets or accounts.

It is important to keep this financial information up to date, as changes in bank accounts, credit cards, loans, and investments can happen frequently. This information can be used to help manage the person's finances in case of incapacity or to help their executor handle their finances after they pass away.

Bank Information

Bank information is an important part of the financial information section in a personal information document. Here are some details that can be included under this section:

- **Name of the bank:** This includes the name of the bank where the person holds their account.

- **Account number:** This includes the account number of the person's bank account(s).

- **Account type:** This includes information about the type of account, such as savings, checking, or money market.

- **Current balance:** This includes the current balance of the account(s).

It is important to keep this information up to date and accurate, as it can be used to manage the person's finances in case of incapacity or to help their executor handle their finances after they pass away. It is also important to keep this information secure and confidential, as it contains sensitive financial information. A personal information document should be stored in a safe and secure location, such as a locked safe or a secure digital file with proper encryption.

Bank Name: _____

Account Type: _____

Account Number: _____

Routing Number: _____

Online Login URL: _____

Online Login Username: _____

Online Login Password: _____

Credit Cards

Credit card information is another important aspect of the financial information section in a personal information document. Here are some details that can be included under this section:

- **Credit card issuer:** This includes the name of the credit card issuer, such as Visa, Mastercard, or American Express.

- **Credit card number:** This includes the 16-digit credit card number.

- **Expiration date:** This includes the month and year that the credit card expires.

- **Security code:** This includes the three-digit security code on the back of the credit card.

- **Credit limit:** This includes the maximum amount that can be charged to the credit card.

It is important to keep this information up to date and accurate, as it can be used to manage the person's finances in case of incapacity or to help their executor handle their finances after they pass away. It is also important to keep this information secure and confidential, as it contains sensitive financial information. A personal information document should be stored in a safe and secure location, such as a locked safe or a secure digital file with proper encryption.

Card Issuer: _____

Card Type: _____

Card Number: _____

Expiration Date: _____

Security Code: _____

Balance: _____

Online Login URL: _____

Online Login Username: _____

Online Login Password: _____

Loans

Another aspect of financial information is loans. This can include:

- **Loan issuer:** This includes the name of the institution or organization that issued the loan.

- **Loan type:** This includes the type of loan, such as a mortgage, personal loan, or student loan.

- **Loan balance:** This includes the outstanding balance on the loan.

- **Interest rate:** This includes the interest rate on the loan.

- **Payment schedule:** This includes the frequency and amount of loan payments.

- **Collateral:** This includes any collateral put up for the loan, such as a house or a car.

Keeping track of loan information is important for financial planning and management. It can also be helpful for an executor in settling the person's estate after they pass away. Like with credit card information, it's important to keep loan information secure and confidential. A personal information document should be stored in a safe and secure location, such as a locked safe or a secure digital file with proper encryption.

Lender Name: _____

Lender Type: _____

Loan Amount: _____

Interest Rate: _____

Monthly Payment: _____

Due Date: _____

Remaining Balance: _____

Online Login URL: _____

Online Login Username: _____

Online Login Password: _____

Loans Continued

In addition to the primary loan information that was mentioned earlier, here are a few more details to consider adding:

- **Payment history:** This includes a record of past payments made on the loan.

- **Loan purpose:** This includes why the loan was taken out, such as for a car, education, or home improvement.

- **Loan terms:** This includes the length of the loan and any other terms and conditions associated with it.

- **Co-signers:** If someone else co-signed the loan, it's important to include their name and contact information.

Having a complete record of loans is important not just for financial planning and management, but also in case of unexpected events such as disability or death. In such cases, the executor of the estate may need to contact the loan issuer to make arrangements for payment or transfer of the loan.

Lender Name: _____

Lender Type: _____

Loan Amount: _____

Interest Rate: _____

Monthly Payment: _____

Due Date: _____

Remaining Balance: _____

Online Login URL: _____

Online Login Username: _____

Online Login Password: _____

Lender Name: _____

Lender Type: _____

Loan Amount: _____

Interest Rate: _____

Monthly Payment: _____

Due Date: _____

Remaining Balance: _____

Online Login URL: _____

Online Login Username: _____

Online Login Password: _____

Loans Continued

In addition to the basic loan information that was mentioned earlier, here are a few more details to consider adding:

- **Payment history:** This includes a record of past payments made on the loan.

- **Loan purpose:** This includes why the loan was taken out, such as for a car, education, or home improvement.

- **Loan terms:** This includes the length of the loan and any other terms and conditions associated with it.

- **Co-signers:** If someone else co-signed the loan, it's important to include their name and contact information.

Having a complete record of loans is important not just for financial planning and management, but also in case of unexpected events such as disability or death. In such cases, the executor of the estate may need to contact the loan issuer to make arrangements for payment or transfer of the loan.

Lender Name: _____

Lender Type: _____

Loan Amount: _____

Interest Rate: _____

Monthly Payment: _____

Due Date: _____

Remaining Balance: _____

Online Login URL: _____

Online Login Username: _____

Online Login Password: _____

Investments

When it comes to financial planning, investments can play an important role in building wealth and achieving long-term financial goals. Here are some pieces of information to consider including in your investment section:

- **Investment accounts:** This includes the names and account numbers of any investment accounts, such as brokerage accounts or retirement accounts.

- **Investment holdings:** This includes the specific investments held within each account, such as stocks, bonds, mutual funds, or exchange-traded funds (ETFs).

- **Investment value:** This includes the current value of each investment account and the estimated value of each holding.

- **Investment advisors:** If you work with a financial advisor, it's important to include their name, contact information, and any relevant account numbers or other details.

- **Investment goals:** It can be helpful to include your long-term investment goals, such as retirement or saving for a child's education.

By keeping a comprehensive record of your investment accounts and holdings, you can stay on top of your investment strategy and make informed decisions about your financial future. Additionally, having this information readily available can be helpful for your loved ones in case of incapacity or death.

Investment Firm: _____

Account Type: _____

Account Number: _____

Investment Type: _____

Investment Value: _____

Current Yield: _____

Date of Last Transaction: _____

Balance: _____

Online Login URL: _____

Online Login Username: _____

Online Login Password: _____

Investment Firm: _____

Account Type: _____

Account Number: _____

Investment Type: _____

Investment Value: _____

Current Yield: _____

Date of Last Transaction: _____

Balance: _____

Online Login URL: _____

Online Login Username: _____

Online Login Password: _____

Investments Continued

Here are some additional pieces of information to consider including in the investments section:

- **Investment income:** This includes any income generated by your investments, such as dividends, interest, or capital gains.

- **Investment expenses:** This includes any fees or expenses associated with your investments, such as management fees or trading fees.

- **Investment performance:** This includes the historical performance of your investments, such as annual returns or growth rates.

- **Investment strategy:** This includes your overall investment strategy and approach, such as your risk tolerance, asset allocation, and diversification strategy.

- **Investment documents:** This includes any important investment-related documents, such as account statements, trade confirmations, and tax documents.

By including this information in your investment section, you can have a more comprehensive view of your investment portfolio and strategy. This can be especially helpful when reviewing your investments with a financial advisor or when making investment decisions on your own. Additionally, having this information organized and easily accessible can be helpful for your loved ones in the event of incapacity or death.

Investment Firm: _____

Account Type: _____

Account Number: _____

Investment Type: _____

Investment Value: _____

Current Yield: _____

Date of Last Transaction: _____

Balance: _____

Online Login URL: _____

Online Login Username: _____

Online Login Password: _____

Investment Firm: _____

Account Type: _____

Account Number: _____

Investment Type: _____

Investment Value: _____

Current Yield: _____

Date of Last Transaction: _____

Balance: _____

Online Login URL: _____

Online Login Username: _____

Online Login Password: _____

Insurance Agency

The insurance agency section of a personal information organizer typically includes information about the insurance policies that a person has. This can include details about health insurance, life insurance, car insurance, home insurance, and any other insurance policies that the person holds.

Here are some pieces of information that you may want to include in the insurance agency section:

- **Insurance policy type:** This includes the type of insurance policy that you have, such as health insurance, life insurance, auto insurance, or homeowner's insurance.

- **Insurance provider name:** This includes the name of the insurance company that provides your policy.

- **Policy number:** This is the unique identification number associated with your policy.

- **Policy start and end date:** This includes the dates that your policy started and will end.

- **Policy coverage and limits:** This includes the types of coverage included in your policy and the limits of coverage for each type.

- **Premium amount:** This is the amount of money that you pay for your insurance policy, typically on a monthly or annual basis.

- **Payment information:** This includes information about how you pay your insurance premiums, such as the payment method and due date.

- **Agent contact information:** This includes the name, phone number, and email address of your insurance agent.

By organizing all of your insurance policy information in one place, you can easily keep track of your coverage, premiums, and important contact information. This can be especially helpful in the event of an emergency, where quick access to insurance information may be necessary.

Insurance Company: _____

Policy Type: _____

Policy Number: _____

Coverage: _____

Beneficiary: _____

Online Login URL: _____

Online Login Username: _____

Online Login Password: _____

Insurance Company: _____

Policy Type: _____

Policy Number: _____

Coverage: _____

Beneficiary: _____

Online Login URL: _____

Online Login Username: _____

Online Login Password: _____

Insurance Continued

In the context of the personal finance and estate planning, insurance refers to the various policies a person may hold to protect themselves and their loved ones in the event of unexpected events or accidents. Some common types of insurance include:

- **Life insurance:** provides a payout to designated beneficiaries upon the policyholder's death.

- **Health insurance:** helps cover the costs of medical care and treatment.

- **Homeowner's insurance:** protects the policyholder's home and property in the event of damage or theft.

- **Auto insurance:** covers the policyholder's vehicle in the event of damage or accidents.

- **Disability insurance:** provides income replacement in the event of an illness or injury that prevents the policyholder from working.

- **Long-term care insurance:** covers the costs of long-term care, such as assisted living or nursing home care.

When organizing financial information for estate planning purposes, it is important to include details about insurance policies, such as the policy number, the name of the insurance company, and the contact information for the agent or representative who handles the policy. This information can help ensure that beneficiaries are able to access the benefits they are entitled to in a timely and efficient manner.

Insurance Company: _____

Policy Type: _____

Policy Number: _____

Coverage: _____

Beneficiary: _____

Online Login URL: _____

Online Login Username: _____

Online Login Password: _____

Insurance Company: _____

Policy Type: _____

Policy Number: _____

Coverage: _____

Beneficiary: _____

Online Login URL: _____

Online Login Username: _____

Online Login Password: _____

Insurance Company: _____

Policy Type: _____

Policy Number: _____

Coverage: _____

Beneficiary: _____

Online Login URL: _____

Online Login Username: _____

Online Login Password: _____

Taxes

Taxes are a crucial aspect of personal finance and estate planning. In general, taxes are payments made to the government to support public services and infrastructure, and they are usually assessed based on income, property, and other financial activities. Here are some important aspects of taxes to consider when organizing financial information for estate planning purposes:

- **Income taxes:** Individuals are required to pay taxes on the income they earn from various sources, including wages, salaries, investments, and rental income. Income taxes can vary depending on the amount of income earned and the tax bracket the individual falls into.

- **Property taxes:** Property taxes are assessed on real estate and other property owned by the individual. The amount of property tax owed is usually based on the assessed value of the property.

- **Estate taxes:** When an individual passes away, their estate may be subject to estate taxes, which are taxes assessed on the value of the assets that make up the estate. The threshold for estate taxes varies by state and country.

When organizing financial information for estate planning purposes, it is important to include details about the taxes that the individual is currently paying or may be responsible for in the future. This can include information such as the current tax rate, the amount of taxes owed, and the due date for filing tax returns. Additionally, it is important to consider any tax implications of estate planning decisions, such as how a particular asset may be taxed when it is transferred to a beneficiary.

Tax Year: _____

Filing Status: _____

Filing Deadline: _____

Taxable Income: _____

Deductions: _____

Credits: _____

Tax Owed/Refund: _____

Online Tax Account URL: _____

Online Tax Account Username: _____

Online Tax Account Password: _____

Tax Year: _____

Filing Status: _____

Filing Deadline: _____

Taxable Income: _____

Deductions: _____

Credits: _____

Tax Owed/Refund: _____

Online Tax Account URL: _____

Online Tax Account Username: _____

Online Tax Account Password: _____

Taxes Continued

In the context of personal finances, taxes refer to the money that an individual is required to pay to the government based on their income and other factors. The information related to taxes in a personal information document can include details about the types of taxes that Person 1 owes, such as income tax, property tax, or capital gains tax. It can also include information about any tax deductions, credits, or exemptions that Person 1 is eligible for.

In addition to this, the document can also include information about any past tax returns that Person 1 has filed, along with the contact information for their tax accountant or tax attorney. This information can be useful in the event of an audit or any other tax-related issues that may arise in the future.

Tax Year: _____

Filing Status: _____

Filing Deadline: _____

Taxable Income: _____

Deductions: _____

Credits: _____

Tax Owed/Refund: _____

Online Tax Account URL: _____

Online Tax Account Username: _____

Online Tax Account Password: _____

Tax Year: _____

Filing Status: _____

Filing Deadline: _____

Taxable Income: _____

Deductions: _____

Credits: _____

Tax Owed/Refund: _____

Online Tax Account URL: _____

Online Tax Account Username: _____

Online Tax Account Password: _____

Cryptocurrency / Bitcoin Accounts

Cryptocurrency and Bitcoin accounts are digital assets that can hold and transfer value, typically without the need for a central authority or intermediary. In the context of a personal information document, information related to cryptocurrency and Bitcoin accounts can include details about the types of cryptocurrencies that Person 1 owns, the amount of each cryptocurrency, and the location of the wallets or exchanges where the cryptocurrencies are held.

This information can be important for a number of reasons, such as facilitating the transfer of cryptocurrency assets to heirs or beneficiaries in the event of Person 1's death. It can also help to ensure that Person 1's cryptocurrency assets are protected and secure, by providing information about any passwords, private keys, or other security measures that are in place to protect the accounts.

Cryptocurrency or Bitcoin Exchange: _____

Wallet address: _____

Currency Type (e.g. Bitcoin, Ethereum, Solana, Tron etc.): _____

Balance: _____

Private Key: _____

Public Key: _____

Online Login URL: _____

Online Login Username: _____

Online Login Password: _____

Cryptocurrency or Bitcoin Exchange: _____

Wallet address: _____

Currency Type (e.g. Bitcoin, Ethereum, Solana, Tron etc.): _____

Balance: _____

Private Key: _____

Public Key: _____

Online Login URL: _____

Online Login Username: _____

Online Login Password: _____

Cryptocurrency or Bitcoin Exchange: _____

Wallet address: _____

Currency Type (e.g. Bitcoin, Ethereum, Solana, Tron etc.): _____

Balance: _____

Private Key: _____

Public Key: _____

Online Login URL: _____

Online Login Username: _____

Online Login Password: _____

Retirement Accounts (e.g. 401(k), IRA)

Retirement accounts, such as 401(k)s and IRAs, are important financial assets that can help provide for Person 1's financial needs during retirement. In the context of a personal information document, information related to retirement accounts can include the types of accounts that Person 1 has, the account numbers, the names and contact information for the financial institutions that hold the accounts, and any beneficiary information.

Having this information readily available can help to ensure that Person 1's retirement accounts are properly managed and protected. It can also be useful for estate planning purposes, as Person 1 may want to designate specific beneficiaries to receive the funds in the event of their death.

It's important to note that retirement accounts are subject to specific rules and regulations, such as required minimum distributions (RMDs) and early withdrawal penalties. Therefore, it may be helpful for Person 1 to also include information about their retirement goals and plans, so that their beneficiaries or estate executor can make informed decisions about how to manage the accounts.

Account Holder(s): _____

Account Number(s): _____

Institution(s): _____

Beneficiary(ies): _____

Contribution Amount: _____

Investment Allocations: _____

Account Holder(s): _____

Account Number(s): _____

Institution(s): _____

Beneficiary(ies): _____

Contribution Amount: _____

Investment Allocations: _____

Account Holder(s): _____

Account Number(s): _____

Institution(s): _____

Beneficiary(ies): _____

Contribution Amount: _____

Investment Allocations: _____

Pension Plans

A pension plan is a type of retirement plan where an employer promises to pay a fixed amount of income to an employee after they retire. Pension plans are typically funded by the employer, although employees may also contribute to their own pension plan.

In a pension plan, the employer makes contributions to a fund on behalf of the employee, and the money is invested to generate income over time. When the employee reaches retirement age, they receive regular payments from the pension plan.

Pension plans can be either defined benefit plans or defined contribution plans. In a defined benefit plan, the employer guarantees the employee a specific amount of retirement income. In a defined contribution plan, the employer contributes a fixed amount to the employee's retirement account, and the employee is responsible for managing the investments and deciding how to withdraw the money in retirement.

It's important to keep track of pension plans and include them in your financial information in case of unexpected events such as disability or death, and to ensure that your beneficiaries receive the appropriate benefits.

Plan Name: _____

Plan Administrator: _____

Benefit Amount: _____

Payment Frequency: _____

Beneficiary(ies): _____

Vesting Information: _____

Pension Plan 2

Plan Name: _____

Plan Administrator: _____

Benefit Amount: _____

Payment Frequency: _____

Beneficiary(ies): _____

Vesting Information: _____

Pension Plan 3

Plan Name: _____

Plan Administrator: _____

Benefit Amount: _____

Payment Frequency: _____

Beneficiary(ies): _____

Vesting Information: _____

Stock Options

Stock options are a form of compensation given to employees by their employer, allowing them to buy company stock at a set price within a specific time frame. They are a type of financial instrument that gives the holder the right to buy or sell a specific amount of stock at a certain price, known as the strike price.

In the context of personal finance and estate planning, it is important to document any stock options that you may have, including the number of options, the strike price, and the expiration date. It is also important to document any beneficiaries or heirs who may be entitled to these options in the event of your death.

It is recommended to consult with a financial advisor or estate planning attorney to determine the best course of action for managing and distributing stock options as part of your estate plan.

Stock Options

Company Name: _____

Option Grant Date(s): _____

Option Expiration Date(s): _____

Number of Shares: _____

Strike Price: _____

Vesting Schedule: _____

Stock Options 2

Company Name: _____

Option Grant Date(s): _____

Option Expiration Date(s): _____

Number of Shares: _____

Strike Price: _____

Vesting Schedule: _____

Stock Options 3

Company Name: _____

Option Grant Date(s): _____

Option Expiration Date(s): _____

Number of Shares: _____

Strike Price: _____

Vesting Schedule: _____

Social Security Information

Social Security Information refers to the details related to an individual's Social Security benefits, including their Social Security number, benefit statement, and other relevant documentation.

The Social Security Administration (SSA) provides benefits to retired, disabled, or deceased individuals and their eligible dependents. To receive Social Security benefits, individuals must have a Social Security number, which is a unique nine-digit identification number issued by the SSA.

In addition to the Social Security number, individuals should keep a record of their Social Security benefit statement, which outlines their estimated future retirement, disability, and survivor benefits. It's important to review this statement periodically to ensure the information is accurate and up-to-date.

Individuals who are eligible for Social Security benefits should also keep track of any documentation related to their benefits, including their application for benefits and any correspondence with the SSA. This information can be crucial in case of any issues or disputes with the SSA.

Overall, including Social Security Information in an important document or an estate plan can help ensure that an individual's benefits are protected and allocated according to their wishes.

Social Security Number(s): _____

Statement(s) of Benefits: _____

Survivor Benefits: _____

Disability Benefits: _____

Trusts

A trust is a legal arrangement where an individual, known as the trustor or grantor, transfers their assets or property to a trustee, who manages and distributes the assets to the beneficiaries according to the terms outlined in the trust agreement. Trusts can be established for a variety of reasons, such as to avoid probate, minimize estate taxes, protect assets, and provide for beneficiaries.

In a trust, the trustor establishes the terms of the trust, including the beneficiaries, the assets to be included, and the rules for distribution. The trustee, who can be an individual or a financial institution, manages the trust assets and ensures that they are distributed according to the trust terms. The beneficiaries are the individuals or organizations who receive the benefits of the trust, such as income or assets.

There are several types of trusts, including revocable living trusts, irrevocable trusts, charitable trusts, and special needs trusts. The type of trust chosen will depend on the specific goals and needs of the trustor.

It is important to include information about trusts in an estate plan so that beneficiaries are aware of their existence and can receive the benefits intended for them. This can include details about the assets included in the trust, the trustee's contact information, and instructions for how the trust should be managed and distributed.

Trust Name: _____

Trustee(s): _____

Beneficiary(ies): _____

Trust Assets: _____

Trust Terms and Conditions: _____

Trust Name: _____

Trustee(s): _____

Beneficiary(ies): _____

Trust Assets: _____

Trust Terms and Conditions: _____

Trust Name: _____

Trustee(s): _____

Beneficiary(ies): _____

Trust Assets: _____

Trust Terms and Conditions: _____

Business Interest

Business interest refers to an individual's ownership in a business or businesses. This can include sole proprietorships, partnerships, limited liability companies (LLCs), and corporations. In the context of an estate plan, an individual may have business interests that need to be addressed in their will or other legal documents.

It is important to provide details of the business interests in the estate plan, such as the name of the business, the type of ownership interest, and any relevant financial information. This can help ensure that the business interest is handled in accordance with the individual's wishes after they pass away.

For example, if an individual owns a significant percentage of a family business, they may want to specify in their will how their interest in the business should be distributed among family members or other heirs. Alternatively, they may want to provide instructions for the sale or transfer of the business interest after their death.

Business interests can also have tax implications, so it is important to consult with an attorney or financial advisor when including them in an estate plan.

Business Name: _____

Business Type: _____

Percentage of Ownership: _____

Value of Ownership: _____

Business Contacts: _____

Business Documents: _____

Business Name: _____

Business Type: _____

Percentage of Ownership: _____

Value of Ownership: _____

Business Contacts: _____

Business Documents: _____

Business Name: _____

Business Type: _____

Percentage of Ownership: _____

Value of Ownership: _____

Business Contacts: _____

Business Documents: _____

Vehicle(s)

Sure, when it comes to the section on vehicles in a personal information document, it typically includes information on any vehicles that belong to the individual, including cars, trucks, motorcycles, boats, and other types of vehicles.

Some of the information that may be included in this section can include:

- The make, model, year, and color of each vehicle

- The license plate number and state

- The vehicle identification number (VIN)

- The current location of the vehicle

- The estimated value of the vehicle

- Any outstanding loans or liens on the vehicle

Having this information in a personal information document can be helpful in case of an emergency, such as a car accident, or if the individual becomes unable to manage their affairs due to illness or incapacity. It can also be useful when it comes to estate planning, as the information can be used to ensure that the individual's assets are distributed according to their wishes after their passing.

Vehicle: _____

Value: _____

(VIN):

Vehicle Id Number: _____

License Plate Number: _____

Annual Registration: _____

Auto Insurance

Account Number: _____

Due Date: _____

Amount: _____

Payment Method: _____

Notes: _____

_____

Vehicle: _____

Value: _____

(VIN):

Vehicle Id Number: _____

License Plate Number: _____

Annual Registration: _____

Auto Insurance

Account Number: _____

Due Date: _____

Amount: _____

Payment Method: _____

Notes: _____

_____

Vehicle(s) Continued

In the context of personal information management, the section on vehicle(s) typically includes information on all owned vehicles, including cars, trucks, motorcycles, RVs, and boats. This information may include the make and model of the vehicle, the year it was manufactured, its license plate number, registration information, and any loans or liens against the vehicle.

Other important details that may be included in this section are the vehicle identification number (VIN), purchase price, insurance information, and maintenance records. It may also be helpful to include any upgrades or modifications made to the vehicle, as well as its current value.

Having this information readily available can be useful in a variety of situations, such as when applying for car insurance, selling the vehicle, or filing a police report in case of theft. Additionally, keeping track of maintenance and repairs can help ensure the vehicle stays in good condition and maintains its value.

Vehicle: _____

Value: _____

(VIN):

Vehicle Id Number: _____

License Plate Number: _____

Annual Registration: _____

Auto Insurance

Account Number: _____

Due Date: _____

Amount: _____

Payment Method: _____

Notes: _____

Vehicle: _____

Value: _____

(VIN):

Vehicle Id Number: _____

License Plate Number: _____

Annual Registration: _____

Auto Insurance

Account Number: _____

Due Date: _____

Amount: _____

Payment Method: _____

Notes: _____

Real Estate and Property

Real estate and property refer to any land, buildings, or other physical assets that a person owns. This can include:

- **Home:** This refers to the primary residence of the person. The information can include the address, the purchase price, mortgage information, and other relevant details.

- **Rental Properties:** If a person owns rental properties, they should include information such as the address, rental income, expenses, and mortgage information.

- **Land:** This can include any undeveloped property, such as a plot of land that a person owns. The information should include the location, the size, and any relevant details about the property.

- **Vehicles:** This section can include information about any vehicles that the person owns, such as cars, motorcycles, boats, or recreational vehicles. The information should include the make, model, year, and any relevant details about the vehicle, such as the registration number, insurance information, and maintenance history.

- **Other Assets:** This section can include any other assets that the person owns, such as artwork, jewelry, or collectibles. The information should include the value, location, and any relevant details about the asset.

Home: _____

Asset Type: _____

Value: _____

Location: _____

Ownership Details: _____

Home: _____

Asset Type: _____

Value: _____

Location: _____

Ownership Details: _____

Home: _____

Asset Type: _____

Value: _____

Location: _____

Ownership Details: _____

Rental or Vacation Property

Rental or vacation property refers to any real estate property that an individual owns but does not reside in full-time. It can include a second home, a vacation property, or a rental property.

When creating a document that includes rental or vacation property information, it is important to include the property address, the type of property (such as a condo, townhome, or single-family home), and the current status of the property (whether it is rented out or available for use).

In addition, it can be helpful to include any rental agreements or contracts associated with the property, as well as contact information for any property management companies or rental agents. If the property is rented out, include the rental income and any associated expenses, such as mortgage payments, property taxes, insurance, and maintenance costs.

It is also important to include information on any outstanding mortgages or loans on the property, as well as the current market value of the property. This information can be helpful in making decisions about the property's future, such as whether to sell or continue to rent it out.

Home: _____

Asset Type: _____

Value: _____

Location: _____

Ownership Details: _____

Home: _____

Asset Type: _____

Value: _____

Location: _____

Ownership Details: _____

Home: _____

Asset Type: _____

Value: _____

Location: _____

Ownership Details: _____

Home: _____

Asset Type: _____

Value: _____

Location: _____

Ownership Details: _____

Property 1

"Property 1" usually refers to a specific property or asset that an individual owns or has an interest in. This can include a primary residence, a vacation home, rental property, land, or commercial real estate.

In an important documents binder, the section for "Property 1" would typically include information such as the property address, ownership details, purchase price or current value, mortgage or lien information, and any other relevant details. This section may also include copies of deeds, titles, or other legal documents related to the property.

It is important to keep this information up-to-date and easily accessible in case it is needed for legal or financial reasons.

Type of Property (Apartment, Condo,
House, Land, etc.): _____

Location: _____

Value: _____

Ownership (e.g.
Joint, Husband, Wife): _____

Mortgage Details

Property Mortgage: _____

Lender: _____

Loan Amount: _____

Interest Rate: _____

Term: _____

Monthly Payment: _____

Taxes

Annual Property Tax: _____

Due Date: _____

Maintenance and Repairs: _____

Rental Information

Rental information is typically related to a property that is being rented out to tenants. This information may include details about the property, such as the address, square footage, number of bedrooms and bathrooms, and amenities.

It may also include information about the rental agreement, such as the monthly rent amount, lease term, security deposit, and any other fees or charges associated with renting the property.

Other rental information may include details about the current tenants, such as their names, contact information, and payment history. Landlords may also keep records of maintenance and repairs that have been performed on the property, as well as any issues or complaints that have been reported by tenants.

Overall, rental information is important for both landlords and tenants to keep track of to ensure a smooth and successful rental experience.

Property Name: _____

Property Address: _____

Monthly Rental Income: _____

Tenant Name: _____

Contact Information: _____

Lease Start Date: _____ Lease End Date: _____

Notes or Comments About the Rental Income: _____

_____

_____

Property 2

"Property 2" generally refers to a second piece of real estate or property that the individual owns. This section of the personal information document can include details such as the property's location, the type of property (e.g., residential, commercial), the size of the property, the current market value or purchase price, any outstanding mortgage or liens, and other relevant information about the property. Additionally, this section can also include information on any rental income generated by the property, as well as any associated expenses such as property taxes, insurance, and maintenance costs.

Type of Property (Apartment, Condo,
House, Land, etc.): _____
Location: _____
Value: _____
Ownership (e.g.
Joint, Husband, Wife): _____

Mortgage Details

Property Mortgage: _____
Lender: _____
Loan Amount: _____
Interest Rate: _____
Term: _____
Monthly Payment: _____

Taxes

Annual Property Tax: _____
Due Date: _____
Maintenance and Repairs: _____

Rental Information

Rental information for Property 2 may include details such as:

- **Rental Agreement:** This is a legally binding contract between the landlord and the tenant that outlines the terms and conditions of the rental, including the rental amount, payment due date, lease duration, security deposit, late payment fees, pet policies, maintenance and repairs, and more.

- **Rent Payment:** This section includes details on how much rent is due each month, the payment due date, accepted payment methods, and penalties for late or missed payments.

- **Security Deposit:** This is the amount of money that the tenant pays upfront to the landlord to cover any damages or unpaid rent at the end of the lease. The security deposit amount, terms of use, and refund conditions should be detailed in this section.

- **Utilities:** Information about which utilities are included in the rent, such as water, gas, and electricity, and which ones the tenant is responsible for paying.

- **Maintenance and Repairs:** This section outlines who is responsible for maintenance and repairs, and how requests for repairs should be submitted and handled.

- **Move-In and Move-Out:** This section details the process for moving in and out of the rental property, including any move-in or move-out fees, required cleaning, and procedures for returning keys.

- **Tenant Rights and Responsibilities:** This section outlines the tenant's rights and responsibilities, including the right to quiet enjoyment, the obligation to keep the property clean and undamaged, and restrictions on alterations or modifications.

- **Landlord Rights and Responsibilities:** This section outlines the landlord's rights and responsibilities, such as the right to enter the rental property for inspections or repairs, and the obligation to provide a habitable living environment.

- **Termination of Lease:** This section outlines the terms and conditions for terminating the lease, including notice requirements, penalties for breaking the lease, and procedures for returning the security deposit.

Homeowners Insurance

Homeowners insurance is a type of insurance policy that protects a homeowner's property and belongings in case of damage or loss due to various incidents. This insurance typically covers damage from natural disasters like fire, wind, hail, lightning, and theft, as well as damage to personal property inside the home.

Homeowners insurance policies can vary in terms of coverage and price, and may also include liability coverage for injuries that occur on the property. It is usually required by mortgage lenders as a condition of approving a home loan.

When purchasing homeowners insurance, it is important to carefully review the policy to understand what is covered and what is not. Homeowners should also regularly review and update their policy as needed, and ensure they have adequate coverage to protect their home and assets.

Account Name: _____

Account Number: _____

Due Date: _____ Amount: _____

Payment Method: _____

Account Number: _____

Notes: _____

Account Name: _____

Account Number: _____

Due Date: _____ Amount: _____

Payment Method: _____

Account Number: _____

Notes: _____

Monthly Utilities Property 1

Monthly utilities for a property typically refer to the regular expenses related to essential services such as water, electricity, gas, internet, and cable TV. This information is important to have in a personal information document as it provides an overview of the ongoing expenses that need to be paid to maintain the property. It can also be helpful for budgeting purposes and to ensure that payments are made on time.

The monthly utilities section for a property may include details such as the name of the utility provider, the type of service (e.g., electricity, water), the account number, billing address, due dates, and payment methods. It can also include information on any special arrangements or discounts that are available, such as budget billing or autopay options.

It is essential to keep this information up-to-date, especially if there are changes in service providers or if there are any updates to the account details. This can help avoid any interruption of service or missed payments, which can result in additional fees or even service termination.

Electricity

Account Name: _____

Account Number: _____

Due Date: _____ Amount: _____

Payment Method: _____

Account Number: _____

Notes: _____

Gas/Oil

Account Name: _____

Account Number: _____

Due Date: _____ Amount: _____

Payment Method: _____

Account Number: _____

Notes: _____

Garbage

Account Name: _____

Account Number: _____

Due Date: _____ Amount: _____

Payment Method: _____

Account Number: _____

Notes: _____

Water / Sewer

Account Name: _____

Account Number: _____

Due Date: _____ Amount: _____

Payment Method: _____

Account Number: _____

Notes: _____

Monthly Utilities Property 2

Monthly Utilities for Property 2 refers to the regular bills and expenses related to the property, such as:

- **Electricity:** This includes the cost of using electricity to power the property. The cost of electricity can vary depending on the location and usage.

- **Water:** This includes the cost of using water in the property, including drinking water, wastewater, and any irrigation systems.

- **Gas:** If the property has gas appliances or heating, then there will be a gas bill associated with it. Gas costs can vary depending on usage and location.

- **Internet and Cable:** This includes the cost of any internet and cable services used in the property. The cost of these services can vary depending on the provider and the package selected.

- **Home Security:** If the property has a home security system, there will be a monthly cost associated with it.

- **Waste Disposal:** This includes the cost of trash and recycling services for the property.

- **Homeowner's Association (HOA) fees:** If the property is part of an HOA, there will be monthly fees associated with it. These fees can vary depending on the location and services provided.

- **Property Insurance:** This includes the cost of insuring the property against damages and liabilities.

The amount of these expenses can vary depending on the location and the usage of the property.

Electricity

Account Name: _____

Account Number: _____

Due Date: _____ Amount: _____

Payment Method: _____

Account Number: _____

Notes: _____

Gas/Oil

Account Name: _____

Account Number: _____

Due Date: _____ Amount: _____

Payment Method: _____

Account Number: _____

Notes: _____

Garbage

Account Name: _____

Account Number: _____

Due Date: _____ Amount: _____

Payment Method: _____

Account Number: _____

Notes: _____

Water / Sewer

Account Name: _____

Account Number: _____

Due Date: _____ Amount: _____

Payment Method: _____

Account Number: _____

Notes: _____

Monthly Utilities Property 3

As mentioned earlier, the "Monthly Utilities" subsection typically includes information on the various utility services used by the individual and their corresponding monthly costs. For "Property 3", this would likely include the following:

- **Electricity:** The amount paid each month for the property's electricity usage.

- **Water:** The monthly cost of water usage for the property.

- **Gas:** If the property uses gas for heating or other appliances, the monthly cost would be listed here.

- **Internet/cable/phone:** This would include any monthly charges for internet, cable TV, and/or phone services.

- **Trash:** The cost of waste management and trash pickup for the property.

The specific details and amounts for each utility service would be listed under their respective categories.

Electricity

Account Name: _____

Account Number: _____

Due Date: _____ Amount: _____

Payment Method: _____

Account Number: _____

Notes: _____

Gas/Oil

Account Name: _____

Account Number: _____

Due Date: _____ Amount: _____

Payment Method: _____

Account Number: _____

Notes: _____

Garbage

Account Name: _____

Account Number: _____

Due Date: _____ Amount: _____

Payment Method: _____

Account Number: _____

Notes: _____

Water / Sewer

Account Name: _____

Account Number: _____

Due Date: _____ Amount: _____

Payment Method: _____

Account Number: _____

Notes: _____

Miscellaneous Discretionary Home Expenses

Miscellaneous discretionary home expenses refer to any regular, non-essential expenses that are associated with the home or household. These expenses can vary depending on individual preferences and lifestyle choices. Some common examples of miscellaneous discretionary home expenses are:

- **Internet:** Monthly fees for home internet service, such as cable or fiber optic.

- **Cable:** Monthly fees for cable TV service, which may include access to premium channels or on-demand programming.

- **Streaming services:** Monthly subscription fees for streaming services, such as Netflix, Hulu, or Disney+.

- **Subscriptions (Newspapers/Magazines):** Monthly or annual fees for subscriptions to newspapers or magazines.

- **Gym membership:** Monthly or annual fees for access to a gym or fitness center.

- **Other recurring payments:** Other regular expenses that may be associated with the home, such as landscaping or cleaning services, pet care, or home security services.

It is important to keep track of these expenses as they can add up over time and have a significant impact on personal finances. By including these expenses in a personal record or financial plan, individuals can better manage their budgets and make informed decisions about their discretionary spending.

Account Name: _____

Account Number: _____

Due Date: _____ Amount: _____

Payment Method: _____

Account Number: _____

Notes: _____

Account Name: _____

Account Number: _____

Due Date: _____ Amount: _____

Payment Method: _____

Account Number: _____

Notes: _____

Miscellaneous Discretionary Home Expenses Continued

- Home security system

- Landscaping and lawn care

- Pool maintenance

- Pest control services

- Cleaning services

- Home repairs and maintenance

- Home renovation or improvement projects

- HOA fees

- Property taxes

- Home insurance premiums

- Energy-efficient upgrades

- Furniture and decor purchases

- Artwork and collectibles

- Electronics and gadgets

- Hobby or sports equipment

- Clothing and accessories storage or maintenance (such as dry cleaning)

- Special occasion expenses (such as birthday or holiday decorations)

- Personal care services (such as hairstyling or manicures)

- Entertainment expenses (such as movie or concert ticket)

Chapter 11:

HEALTH & MEDICAL INFORMATION

———

The section of Health & Medical Information is an important part of a personal information document that provides information about a person's medical history, current health status, and future health care preferences. This information is important for medical professionals in case of emergency situations or if a person is unable to make medical decisions for themselves.

The subsections for this section can include:

- **Medical Conditions:** This section lists any medical conditions a person has, such as diabetes, heart disease, allergies, etc. It is important to provide details on the type of condition, the date of diagnosis, and any current treatments.

- **Medications:** This section lists all current medications a person is taking, including over-the-counter medications, vitamins, and supplements. It should include the medication name, dosage, and frequency.

- **Allergies:** This section lists any allergies a person has, including food allergies, drug allergies, and environmental allergies.

- **Medical Procedures:** This section lists any medical procedures a person has undergone, such as surgeries, biopsies, or other medical treatments. It should include the date of the procedure, the name of the procedure, and the name of the doctor who performed it.

- **Medical Providers:** This section provides a list of medical providers a person has seen, including doctors, dentists, and other healthcare professionals. It should include the name of the provider, the type of provider, and their contact information.

- **Health Insurance:** This section provides information about a person's health insurance, including the name of the insurance provider, policy number, and contact information. It is important to keep this information up-to-date in case of any changes.

- **Advance Directives:** This section provides information about any advance directives a person has in place, such as a living will or a durable power of attorney for healthcare. These documents outline a person's preferences for medical treatment in case they become unable to make decisions for themselves.

Overall, the Health & Medical Information section is essential for anyone who wants to ensure that their medical needs and preferences are known in case of an emergency situation. It can help medical professionals provide the best possible care and treatment for the person, and give peace of mind to their loved ones.

Full Name: _____

Date of Birth: _____ Blood Type: _____

Height: _____ Weight: _____

Notes: _____

Medical Insurance Information

Insurance Provider: _____

Policy Number: _____

Group Number: _____

Phone Number: _____

Primary Care Physician: _____

Pharmacy: _____

Pharmacy Address: _____

Pharmacy Phone Number: _____

Notes: _____

Medical History

Medical history refers to a record of an individual's past and current health conditions, illnesses, surgeries, hospitalizations, allergies, medications, and treatments. This information is important for healthcare providers to make informed decisions about an individual's care, as it helps them understand any existing medical conditions, potential complications, and any medications or treatments that may interact with the current course of treatment.

When documenting medical history, it is important to include details such as the name of the condition, date of diagnosis, severity, medications taken, treatments received, and any hospitalizations or surgeries related to the condition. It is also important to document any allergies or adverse reactions to medications or treatments.

Medical history can be divided into several categories, including personal medical history, family medical history, and social history. Personal medical history refers to an individual's own health history, while family medical history refers to the health history of blood relatives. Social history includes information about an individual's lifestyle habits such as smoking, alcohol consumption, and exercise habits, as these factors can impact an individual's overall health.

It is important to keep an updated and accurate medical history record, as this can help healthcare providers make informed decisions about an individual's care and potentially prevent medical errors or complications.

Chronic Illnesses/Conditions: _____

Continued: _____

Continued: _____

Continued: _____

Continued: _____

Surgeries or Hospitalizations: _____

Continued: _____

Continued: _____

Continued: _____

Continued: _____

Family Medical History: _____

Continued: _____

Continued: _____

Continued: _____

Continued: _____

Medication Allergies: _____

Continued: _____

Continued: _____

Continued: _____

Continued: _____

Current Medications: _____

Continued: _____

Continued: _____

Continued: _____

Continued: _____

Medical Emergency(s)

Medical Emergency(s) refer to any unexpected or life-threatening medical situation that may arise, and the steps to be taken to address them. In this section of a personal information document, individuals may provide information on their medical emergency contacts, including their primary care physician, emergency contact person(s), and any other pertinent information that could be useful in the event of a medical emergency. This information may include details on allergies, medications, ongoing medical treatments, and any other medical issues that may require immediate attention. By providing this information, individuals can ensure that their medical needs are addressed promptly and efficiently, even if they are unable to communicate their needs directly. This information can also be useful to medical personnel during an emergency, providing them with crucial information to make informed decisions about a person's medical care.

Emergency Contacts (1)

Name: _____

Relationship: _____

Address: _____

Phone Number: _____

Emergency Contacts (2)

Name: _____

Relationship: _____

Address: _____

Phone Number: _____

Primary Care Physician

Clinic Name: _____

Physician Name: _____

Assistant's Name: _____

Address: _____

Phone Number: _____

Notes: _____

Secondary Care Physician

Clinic Name: _____

Physician Name: _____

Assistant's Name: _____

Address: _____

Phone Number: _____

Notes: _____

Medical Specialists

Medical Specialists refer to healthcare professionals who have specialized education and training in a particular area of medicine or surgery. They are experts in their field and can diagnose, treat and manage complex medical conditions related to their area of expertise. Some examples of medical specialists include:

- **Cardiologists:** A cardiologist specializes in diagnosing and treating heart diseases and conditions related to the cardiovascular system.

- **Neurologists:** A neurologist specializes in the diagnosis and treatment of diseases and conditions that affect the brain, spinal cord, and nervous system.

- **Oncologists:** An oncologist specializes in the diagnosis and treatment of cancer.

- **Gastroenterologists:** A gastroenterologist specializes in diagnosing and treating conditions related to the digestive system, including the esophagus, stomach, intestines, liver, and pancreas.

- **Endocrinologists:** An endocrinologist specializes in the diagnosis and treatment of disorders related to hormones and the endocrine system, including diabetes, thyroid disorders, and hormonal imbalances.

- **Pulmonologists:** A pulmonologist specializes in the diagnosis and treatment of conditions related to the respiratory system, including asthma, chronic obstructive pulmonary disease (COPD), and lung cancer.

- **Rheumatologists:** A rheumatologist specializes in the diagnosis and treatment of autoimmune disorders and conditions related to joints, muscles, and bones, such as arthritis.

- **Dermatologists:** A dermatologist specializes in the diagnosis and treatment of conditions related to the skin, hair, and nails, including acne, eczema, and psoriasis.

- **Psychiatrists:** A psychiatrist specializes in the diagnosis and treatment of mental health disorders, including depression, anxiety, and bipolar disorder.

It's important to have a list of medical specialists you or your family members regularly see to ensure prompt medical attention and care when needed.

Specialists (1)

Clinic Name: _____

Physician Name: _____

Address: _____

Phone Number: _____

Reason for Specialist: _____

Specialists (2)

Clinic Name: _____

Physician Name: _____

Address: _____

Phone Number: _____

Reason for Specialist: _____

Specialists (3)

Clinic Name: _____

Physician Name: _____

Address: _____

Phone Number: _____

Reason for Specialist: _____

Specialists (4)

Clinic Name: _____

Physician Name: _____

Address: _____

Phone Number: _____

Other Medical Providers

Other medical providers refer to health professionals who are not medical specialists but still provide essential medical services. These may include primary care physicians, nurse practitioners, physician assistants, chiropractors, physical therapists, occupational therapists, speech therapists, and mental health professionals such as psychologists and psychiatrists.

It is important to include contact information for all medical providers in this section so that they can be easily reached in case of emergencies or for routine appointments. It is also essential to keep this information updated regularly, especially if there are any changes in the medical provider's contact information or if a new provider is added to the list.

Dental

Insurance Provider: _____

Policy Number: _____

Clinic Name: _____

Dentist Name: _____

Assistant's Name: _____

Address: _____

Phone Number: _____

Notes: _____

Vision

Insurance Provider: _____

Policy Number: _____

Clinic Name: _____

Optometrist Name: _____

Assistant's Name: _____

Address: _____

Phone Number: _____

Notes: _____

Mental Health

Insurance Provider: _____

Policy Number: _____

Clinic Name: _____

Therapist Name: _____

Assistant's Name: _____

Address: _____

Phone Number: _____

Notes: _____

Living Will: (Yes/No)

Agent Name: _____

Durable Power of Attorney for Health Care: (Yes/No)

Name of Power of Attorney for Medical Decisions: _____

Physician Orders for Life-Sustaining Treatment (POLST) (Yes/No)

Do Not Resuscitate Orders (DNR): (Yes/No)

Organ Donor: (Yes/No)

Exceptions: _____

Tissue Donor: (Yes/No)

Exceptions: _____

Advance Directives

Advance directives are legal documents that allow individuals to make decisions about their future medical care, in case they become unable to do so themselves. Advance directives usually come into play if a person is terminally ill or permanently unconscious. There are several types of advance directives, including:

- **Living Will:** A living will is a document that outlines a person's wishes for end-of-life medical care. It specifies the types of medical treatments a person wants or does not want if they become unable to make decisions for themselves.

- **Durable Power of Attorney for Health Care:** A durable power of attorney for health care allows a person to appoint someone else to make medical decisions for them if they become unable to do so themselves. This person is called a healthcare proxy or agent.

- **Do Not Resuscitate (DNR) Order:** A DNR order is a medical order that instructs healthcare providers not to perform cardiopulmonary resuscitation (CPR) in the event of cardiac or respiratory arrest.

It is important for individuals to discuss their end-of-life wishes with their loved ones and healthcare providers and to ensure that their advance directives are up to date and legally valid.

Chapter 12:

MEDICATIONS TO-GO PAGE

———

A Medications To-Go Page is a document that contains important information about the medications a person is currently taking or has been prescribed. This page is usually kept in a portable format, such as a card or small booklet, that can be easily carried by the person in case of an emergency or when visiting a healthcare provider.

The information typically included on a Medications To-Go Page may include the person's name, date of birth, and contact information, as well as a list of all prescription medications they are taking, including the name of the medication, dosage, frequency, and the reason for taking it. It may also include a list of over-the-counter medications, vitamins, or supplements the person is taking.

Having a Medications To-Go Page can be particularly useful when a person is visiting a new healthcare provider, traveling, or in an emergency situation where they are unable to communicate their medical history and current medications. It can help healthcare providers make informed decisions about treatment, avoid potentially harmful drug interactions, and ensure that the person receives appropriate care.

Medication Name: _____

Purpose: _____

Dosage: _____

Date Last Filled: _____

Prescribing Physician: _____

Medication Name: _____

Purpose: _____

Dosage: _____

Date Last Filled: _____

Prescribing Physician: _____

Medication Name: _____

Purpose: _____

Dosage: _____

Date Last Filled: _____

Prescribing Physician: _____

Medication Name: _____

Purpose: _____

Dosage: _____

Date Last Filled: _____

Prescribing Physician: _____

Medication Name: _____

Purpose: _____

Dosage: _____

Date Last Filled: _____

Prescribing Physician: _____

Medication Name: _____

Purpose: _____

Dosage: _____

Date Last Filled: _____

Prescribing Physician: _____

Medication Name: _____

Purpose: _____

Dosage: _____

Date Last Filled: _____

Prescribing Physician: _____

Medication Name: _____

Purpose: _____

Dosage: _____

Date Last Filled: _____

Prescribing Physician: _____

Medication Name: _____

Purpose: _____

Dosage: _____

Date Last Filled: _____

Prescribing Physician: _____

Note: Please make sure to update this list regularly and keep it with you at all times in case of emergencies.

Chapter 13:

PASSWORDS & PROTECTED INFORMATION

To elaborate, the Passwords & Protected Information section of a personal organizer is a place to keep track of all your electronic passwords and login credentials for online accounts and services, such as email accounts, social media accounts, online banking, and other digital services. This section should be kept secure and should only be accessible to individuals authorized to access it.

It's essential to update the passwords and login credentials regularly to prevent unauthorized access to your accounts. You may also want to consider using a password manager to generate and store complex passwords securely.

It's important to note that including sensitive information like passwords in a physical personal organizer carries some risks. If you lose the organizer or it falls into the wrong hands, your personal information could be compromised. To mitigate this risk, you may want to consider storing your electronic passwords and login credentials in an encrypted digital file or using a secure password manager with two-factor authentication.

Electronic Passwords and Online Accounts

In this section of a personal information organizer, you can record all of your usernames and passwords for online accounts and digital services. This can include things like email accounts, social media accounts, online banking and investment accounts, e-commerce sites, and more. It's important to keep this information up to date and secure, as it can be a valuable target for hackers or other cyber threats.

Some tips for managing your electronic passwords and online accounts include:

- **Use unique, strong passwords for each account:** Avoid using the same password for multiple accounts, and use a mix of letters, numbers, and special characters to create strong passwords.

- **Enable two-factor authentication:** Many online services now offer two-factor authentication, which requires an additional code or prompt to access your account, in addition to your password.

- **Use a password manager:** Consider using a password manager to securely store and generate strong passwords for your accounts.

- **Update your passwords regularly:** Make sure to update your passwords every few months, or immediately if you suspect that an account may have been compromised.

- **Be cautious with sharing login information:** Avoid sharing your login information with others, and only provide it when necessary and to trusted sources.

Please fill in the information as applicable.

Email

Email is a system for exchanging messages electronically over a computer network, typically the internet. It allows users to send and receive messages, attachments, and other types of digital content to one or more recipients. Email can be accessed through various platforms such as web-based clients, desktop clients, and mobile apps, and it has become an essential tool for communication in both personal and professional settings. Some of the most popular email services include Gmail, Yahoo Mail, and Microsoft Outlook.

URL: _____

Type of Account: _____

Username: _____

Password: _____

Notes: _____

Email Continued

In addition to the email account credentials, this section may also include information on email providers, email settings, and other related details. Here are some examples of what can be included:

- **Email provider:** This refers to the company or service that provides the email account, such as Google, Microsoft, or Yahoo.

- **Email address:** The email address associated with the account.

- **Username:** Some email services require a username in addition to the email address.

- **Password:** The password associated with the account. It's important to keep this information secure and up to date.

- **Email settings:** This includes information on how the email account is set up, such as the incoming and outgoing server settings, port numbers, and encryption settings.

- **Email forwarding:** If you have set up email forwarding to another email address, it's important to include this information.

- **Spam filter settings:** This includes information on how the email service filters spam and unwanted messages.

- **Recovery options:** Some email services provide recovery options, such as security questions or a secondary email address, in case you forget your password or get locked out of your account.

It's important to keep this information up to date and secure, as email accounts often contain sensitive and confidential information.

URL: _____

Type of Account: _____

Username: _____

Password: _____

Notes: _____

URL: _____

Type of Account: _____

Username: _____

Password: _____

Notes: _____

URL: _____

Type of Account: _____

Username: _____

Password: _____

Notes: _____

URL: _____

Type of Account: _____

Username: _____

Password: _____

Notes: _____

Online Shopping

The "Online Shopping" subsection of "Electronic Passwords and Online Accounts" refers to any accounts you may have with online retailers or e-commerce websites. This could include accounts with Amazon, eBay, Walmart, or any other online store you regularly use to purchase goods or services. It's important to keep track of the login credentials for these accounts so you can easily access them and manage your orders. Additionally, you may want to keep track of any payment methods you have stored on these sites for quick and easy checkout.

URL: _____

Type of Account: _____

Username: _____

Password: _____

Notes: _____

URL: _____

Type of Account: _____

Username: _____

Password: _____

Notes: _____

URL: _____

Type of Account: _____

Username: _____

Password: _____

Notes: _____

Social Media

Social media refers to online platforms and tools that enable users to create, share, and participate in online communities or networks. These platforms allow users to create and share content, interact with others, and follow accounts or pages of interest.

In the context of a personal record or information, listing social media accounts can be helpful in case of emergencies or as a reference for loved ones who may need to access your accounts. It may also be useful for estate planning purposes to have a comprehensive list of all your online profiles and accounts.

Examples of social media platforms include Facebook, Twitter, Instagram, LinkedIn, Snapchat, and TikTok.

URL: _____

Type of Account: _____

Username: _____

Password: _____

Notes: _____

URL: _____

Type of Account: _____

Username: _____

Password: _____

Notes: _____

URL: _____

Type of Account: _____

Username: _____

Password: _____

Notes: _____

URL: _____

Type of Account: _____

Username: _____

Password: _____

Notes: _____

Medical Accounts Online

Medical accounts online refer to any online portals or websites related to your medical care, such as patient portals, health insurance portals, or telemedicine platforms. These platforms can provide access to important medical information, such as medical records, test results, appointment scheduling, and prescription refills. It is important to keep your login information for these accounts secure, as they may contain sensitive personal and medical information. You may also want to check with your healthcare provider to see what online portals or services they offer and how to access them securely.

URL: _____

Type of Account: _____

Username: _____

Password: _____

Notes: _____

URL: _____

Type of Account: _____

Username: _____

Password: _____

Notes: _____

URL: _____

Type of Account: _____

Username: _____

Password: _____

Notes: _____

URL: _____

Type of Account: _____

Username: _____

Password: _____

Notes: _____

URL: _____

Type of Account: _____

Username: _____

Password: _____

Notes: _____

Website / Service

In the context of passwords and protected information, the "Website / Service" section refers to any online service or website that you have an account with and may need to access in the future. This could include:

- Banking websites

- Investment accounts

- Insurance accounts

- Social media accounts

- Email accounts

- Online shopping accounts

- Streaming services

- Gaming accounts

- Educational accounts

- Healthcare accounts

- Government accounts

- Any other online accounts you use

For each website or service, you should include the following information:

- The name of the website or service

- Your username or login ID

- Your password

- Any additional security information, such as security questions or two-factor authentication settings

- Any notes or details about the account, such as the date it was created or the purpose of the account

It's important to keep this information secure, as it can provide access to your sensitive personal and financial information. You may want to consider using a password manager or other secure method to store this information. Additionally, be sure to update your passwords regularly and use strong, unique passwords for each account.

URL: _____

Type of Account: _____

Username: _____

Password: _____

Notes: _____

URL: _____

Type of Account: _____

Username: _____

Password: _____

Notes: _____

URL: _____

Type of Account: _____

Username: _____

Password: _____

Notes: _____

In addition to online accounts, you can also include any physical safes or safety deposit boxes that you have and their corresponding access information.

Safe / Safety Deposit Box

A safe deposit box is a secure container, typically located in a bank or a credit union, where people can store valuables, important documents, and other items that they want to protect from theft, fire, or natural disasters. The box is usually made of steel and can only be opened with a key or combination provided to the owner. The bank or credit union provides access to the box, typically during regular business hours, and may also provide insurance for the contents of the box.

People use safe deposit boxes to store a variety of items, such as important legal documents (e.g., birth certificates, wills, and deeds), family heirlooms, jewelry, and cash. Some people also use them to store copies of important data (e.g., photographs or computer backups) or other items that they don't want to keep at home.

It's important to note that safe deposit boxes are not FDIC-insured. This means that if the bank or credit union where you have a safe deposit box goes out of business or is robbed, you may not be able to recover the contents of your box. Therefore, it's a good idea to make sure that your valuables and important documents are also backed up and stored in a secure location at home or with a trusted family member or friend.

Type of Account: _____

Name on Account: _____

Access Information: _____

Location: _____

Notes: _____

Type of Account: _____

Name on Account: _____

Access Information: _____

Location: _____

Notes: _____

Type of Account: _____

Name on Account: _____

Access Information: _____

Location: _____

Notes: _____

Make sure to keep this information secure and share it only with trusted individuals. It's also important to update this information regularly as passwords and access information may change over time.

Chapter 14:
LEGAL DOCUMENTS & INFORMATION

———

Legal Documents — Husband, Wife or Partner

Legal documents related to marriage or partnership may include:

- **Marriage certificate:** This is the document that legally proves you are married. It is typically issued by the state or county where you were married

- **Prenuptial agreement:** This is a legal document that outlines how assets and debts will be divided in the event of a divorce. It is signed before marriage.

- **Postnuptial agreement:** This is similar to a prenuptial agreement but is signed after marriage.

- **Will:** This legal document outlines how your assets will be distributed after your death.

- **Trust:** A trust is a legal arrangement that allows a third party (the trustee) to hold assets on behalf of a beneficiary.

- **Power of attorney:** This legal document grants someone the authority to act on your behalf in financial or legal matters.

- **Health care proxy:** This legal document designates someone to make medical decisions on your behalf if you are unable to do so.

It's important to keep these documents in a safe and secure location, such as a fireproof safe or safety deposit box at a bank. It's also a good idea to make copies and give them to trusted family members or an attorney. If any of these documents are lost or stolen, it's important to take steps to replace them as soon as possible.

(Be sure to replace lost or stolen documents)

Power of Attorney

Name of Attorney-in-Fact: _____

Location of Original Document: _____

Contact Information of Lawyer: _____

Living Will

Name of Proxy: _____

Treatment Preferences: _____

Location of Original Document: _____

Contact Information of Lawyer: _____

Will

Name of Executor: _____

Name of Beneficiaries: _____

  Continued: _____

  Continued: _____

  Continued: _____

  Continued: _____

Location of Original Document: _____

Contact Information of Lawyer: _____

Cohabitation Agreement

Date Signed: _____

Location of Original Document: _____

Contact Information of Lawyer: _____

Prenuptial Agreement

Date Signed: _____

Location of Original Document: _____

Contact Information of Lawyer: _____

Other Legal Documents

Here are some other legal documents that you may want to consider including in your records:

- **Wills and trusts:** These documents specify how you want your assets distributed after you die. You may also want to include any relevant documentation for trusts you have established.

- **Powers of attorney:** These documents designate a trusted individual to make decisions on your behalf in the event that you are unable to do so.

- **Living will:** This document outlines your wishes for end-of-life care and can provide guidance to your loved ones and medical professionals in the event of a medical emergency.

- **Property deeds and titles:** These documents prove ownership of real estate and other significant assets.

- **Marriage or divorce certificates:** These documents prove your marital status and can be important for things like obtaining government benefits or changing your name.

- **Adoption papers:** These documents are important if you have adopted a child, as they establish your legal relationship with the child.

- **Business formation documents:** If you own a business, you will want to include any relevant documentation such as articles of incorporation, partnership agreements, or operating agreements.

It is important to keep these documents in a safe and secure location, such as a fireproof safe or safety deposit box, and to make sure your loved ones know where to find them in the event of an emergency.

Description: _____

Location of Original Document: _____

Contact Information of Lawyer: _____

Notes: _____

_____

_____

Passport

A passport is an official government-issued document that verifies the identity and nationality of the person holding it. It is typically used for international travel, as it allows the holder to cross borders and enter foreign countries.

Passports usually contain the following information about the holder:

- Full name
- Date of birth
- Place of birth
- Passport number
- Photo of the holder
- Signature of the holder
- Expiration date

To obtain a passport, you must apply through the government agency responsible for issuing them in your country of citizenship. This typically involves filling out an application, providing identification and proof of citizenship, and paying a fee.

It's important to keep your passport in a safe and secure place, as losing it can be a significant inconvenience, and replacing it can be costly and time-consuming. Many people choose to store their passport in a safe or safety deposit box when not in use.

Passport Number: _____

Country of Origin: _____

Website: _____

Phone Number: _____

Where to Report Lost/Stolen: _____

Process to Replace: _____

_____

_____

Driver's License

A driver's license is an official government-issued document that authorizes an individual to operate a motor vehicle. It serves as proof of identity and establishes that the individual has completed the necessary requirements to legally operate a motor vehicle.

The requirements to obtain a driver's license may vary by state or country, but generally include a written exam, a driving skills test, and a vision test. The license typically needs to be renewed every few years and may require additional testing or documentation.

It's important to keep your driver's license information up to date and ensure that you have a valid license at all times when driving. If you lose your license or it gets stolen, it's important to report it to the appropriate authorities and take steps to obtain a replacement.

License Number: _____

State of Issuance: _____

Website: _____

Phone Number: _____

Where to Report Lost/Stolen: _____

Process to Replace: _____

Social Security Card

A Social Security card is a vital record that contains a unique nine-digit number assigned to every citizen, permanent resident, and temporary worker in the United States. The Social Security number (SSN) is used to track a person's earnings and work history to determine their eligibility for Social Security benefits. It is also used for tax purposes, to report wages and self-employment income to the Internal Revenue Service (IRS), and for other purposes such as opening bank accounts or applying for credit.

If you lose your Social Security card, you should request a replacement card from the Social Security Administration (SSA) as soon as possible. To obtain a replacement card, you will need to provide certain documents to prove your identity, age, and citizenship or immigration status. It's important to keep your Social Security card in a safe place and to avoid carrying it with you unless necessary to prevent identity theft.

Social Security Number: _____

State of Issuance: _____

Website: _____

Phone Number: _____

Where to Report Lost/Stolen: _____

Process to Replace: _____

_____

_____

Birth Certificate

A birth certificate is a legal document that serves as proof of a person's identity and citizenship. It includes information such as the individual's full name, date and place of birth, parents' names, and other vital information. Birth certificates are issued by the government in the state or country where the individual was born, and they are often required for a variety of purposes, including obtaining a passport, enrolling in school or the military, and applying for government benefits. It's important to keep a copy of your birth certificate in a safe and secure place, and to have an additional copy in case the original is lost or damaged.

License Number: _____

State of Issuance: _____

Website: _____

Phone Number: _____

Where to Report Lost/Stolen: _____

Process to Replace: _____

_____

_____

Mariage Certificate

A marriage certificate is a legal document that proves a couple is legally married. It typically includes the full names of both spouses, the date and location of the marriage, and the name and signature of the person who performed the ceremony. This document is typically issued by the county or state where the marriage took place. A marriage certificate can be important for a variety of reasons, such as changing your name, applying for a joint loan, or proving your marital status for legal or financial purposes. It is important to keep this document in a safe and secure place, such as a safe or safety deposit box.

License Number: _____

State of Issuance: _____

Website: _____

Phone Number: _____

Where to Report Lost/Stolen: _____

Process to Replace: _____

Misc. Legal Document

Miscellaneous Legal Documents may include but are not limited to:

- **Power of Attorney:** A legal document that grants someone else the authority to act on your behalf for specific matters, such as financial, legal, or healthcare decisions.

- **Living Will/Advance Directive:** A legal document that allows you to specify your medical treatment preferences if you become unable to communicate.

- **Trusts:** A legal arrangement where a trustee holds and manages assets on behalf of a beneficiary.

- **Wills:** A legal document that outlines how you want your assets to be distributed after your death.

- **Property Deeds:** Legal documents that provide proof of ownership of real estate or property.

- **Vehicle Titles:** Legal documents that provide proof of ownership for vehicles.

- **Business Agreements:** Legal documents that outline the terms and conditions of a business transaction or partnership.

It's important to keep these documents safe and secure as they may be needed in legal or emergency situations. Make sure to inform trusted family members or an attorney about the location of these documents.

Misc. Legal Document: _____

Website: _____

Phone Number: _____

Where to Report Lost/Stolen: _____

Process to Replace: _____

_____

_____

Misc. Legal Document: _____

Website: _____

Phone Number: _____

Where to Report Lost/Stolen: _____

Process to Replace: _____

_____

_____

Chapter 15:

IMPORTANT CONTACTS

———

The "Important Contacts" section of a personal information organizer is where you can keep a list of key individuals and organizations that you may need to contact in case of an emergency or other situations. Some examples of contacts you may want to include in this section are:

- **Family members:** You may want to include the names and contact information of your immediate family members, such as parents, siblings, and children.

- **Close friends:** You may want to include the names and contact information of your close friends who you would want to be informed in case of an emergency.

- **Doctors and medical providers:** You should include the names and contact information of your primary care doctor and any other medical specialists you see regularly.

- **Emergency contacts:** This may include the contact information of people you would like to be notified in case of an emergency, such as a trusted neighbor or friend who can take care of your pets or check on your home.

- **Financial advisors and accountants:** You may want to include the contact information of your financial advisor, accountant, or tax preparer.

- **Insurance providers:** You should include the contact information for your various insurance providers, such as your health insurance, life insurance, and home insurance.

- **Legal professionals:** If you have a lawyer, you should include their contact information, as well as any other legal professionals you may work with, such as a notary public or executor of your will.

- **Utility companies**: You may want to include the contact information for your utility companies, such as your electric, gas, water, and phone providers.

- **Government agencies:** You may want to include the contact information for government agencies, such as your local city or county offices, as well as state and federal agencies that you may need to contact.

It's important to keep this section of your personal information organizer up to date, and to make sure that someone you trust knows where to find this information in case of an emergency.

Full Name: _____

Address: _____

City: _____

State: _____ Zip Code: _____

Country: _____

Phone: _____

eMail: _____

Relationship: _____

Full Name: _____

Address: _____

City: _____

State: _____ Zip Code: _____

Country: _____

Phone: _____

eMail: _____

Relationship: _____

Full Name: _____

Address: _____

City: _____

State: _____ Zip Code: _____

Country: _____

Phone: _____

eMail: _____

Relationship: _____

Full Name: _____

Address: _____

City: _____

State: _____ Zip Code: _____

Country: _____

Phone: _____

eMail: _____

Relationship: _____

Chapter 16:

IMPORTANT RESOURCES

———

Important resources refer to the essential contacts, information, and materials that you might need in case of an emergency or other unforeseen circumstances. These resources can include emergency services such as the police, fire department, and hospital, as well as utility companies, insurance providers, and financial institutions.

Some examples of important resources to include in your personal records include:

- **Emergency services:** This includes the phone numbers for the police, fire department, and hospital in your area. If you have specific emergency medical needs or allergies, be sure to include this information as well.

- **Utility companies:** In case of power outages, gas leaks, or other utility emergencies, it's essential to have the contact information for your local utility providers.

- **Insurance providers:** Be sure to include the contact information for your health, home, auto, and other insurance providers in case of an emergency or claim.

- **Financial institutions:** This includes the contact information for your bank, credit card companies, and any other financial institutions you work with. In case of a lost or stolen card, you will need to report it immediately.

- **Local government resources:** Depending on where you live, there may be other important resources to include in your personal records, such as the contact information for your local government offices or community organizations.

Overall, it's important to keep your important resources up to date and easily accessible in case of an emergency or other unforeseen circumstance. Regularly reviewing and updating this information can help ensure that you are prepared for any situation.

Department of Motor Vehicles

The Department of Motor Vehicles (DMV) is a government agency responsible for administering driver's licenses, vehicle registration, and other related services. The DMV is typically responsible for issuing and renewing driver's licenses and ID cards, as well as administering written and road tests. In addition, the DMV is also responsible for registering and titling vehicles, issuing license plates, and maintaining records related to ownership and registration. Some DMVs may also offer additional services, such as issuing disabled parking permits, conducting vehicle inspections, and providing information on traffic safety and regulations. The specific services offered by the DMV may vary by state or jurisdiction.

Department of Motor Vehicles (DMV)

Website for DMV Information

Phone Number for DMV Information

Application Process for Driver's License

Social Security

The Social Security Administration (SSA) is a government agency that administers Social Security benefits, a federal program that provides retirement, disability, and survivor benefits to eligible individuals. The SSA also administers the Supplemental Security Income (SSI) program, which provides financial assistance to individuals with disabilities, people over age 65, and certain other individuals who have limited income and resources.

To access your Social Security information, you can create an online account on the SSA website, which allows you to view your earnings record, estimate your future benefits, and manage your benefits. You can also contact the SSA by phone or visit a local Social Security office to get information about your benefits, apply for benefits, or get help with other Social Security-related issues.

Social Security Administration

Website for Social Security Information

Phone Number for Social Security Information

Application Process for Social Security Benefits

Taxes

Taxes are a mandatory financial obligation imposed by the government on individuals and businesses to fund public services and projects. There are several types of taxes, including income tax, sales tax, property tax, estate tax, and excise tax.

Income tax is a tax levied on an individual's earnings and is calculated based on a percentage of their income. Federal income tax is levied by the U.S. government, while state income tax is levied by individual states.

Sales tax is a tax levied on the sale of goods and services and is usually calculated as a percentage of the purchase price. Sales tax rates vary by state and locality.

Property tax is a tax levied on real estate and other property, such as vehicles or boats, and is calculated based on the assessed value of the property. Property taxes are usually paid to local governments, such as cities or counties.

Estate tax is a tax levied on the value of an individual's estate after they pass away. The tax is calculated based on the fair market value of the assets in the estate and is paid by the estate before it is distributed to the heirs.

Excise tax is a tax levied on the sale of specific goods or services, such as gasoline or tobacco products. The tax is usually included in the price of the goods or services and is paid by the consumer.

Taxes can be complex, and it is important to understand your tax obligations and how to properly file and pay them to avoid penalties and legal issues. It is recommended to seek the assistance of a tax professional or accountant to ensure compliance with tax laws and regulations.

Internal Revenue Service (IRS)

Website for Tax Information

Phone Number for Tax Information

_____

_____

_____

Application Process for Tax Returns

_____

_____

_____

Support Organizations

Support organizations are nonprofit groups that provide assistance, resources, and advocacy for individuals and families facing specific challenges or life situations. These organizations may focus on a particular health condition, disability, demographic group, or social issue.

Examples of support organizations include the American Cancer Society, which provides resources and support for cancer patients and their families, the National Alliance on Mental Illness (NAMI), which advocates for individuals living with mental health conditions and provides resources for support and treatment, and the National Organization for Rare Disorders (NORD), which provides information and advocacy for individuals living with rare diseases and their families.

Support organizations can provide a range of services, including education and awareness, advocacy and policy change, financial assistance and support, and peer support networks. They may also provide referrals to medical professionals, social services, or other relevant resources in the community.

If you or someone you know is facing a particular challenge or life situation, it may be helpful to research and connect with relevant support organizations to access resources, information, and support.

American Cancer Society

The American Cancer Society (ACS) is a nationwide, community-based voluntary health organization that aims to eliminate cancer by funding research, providing patient support, and raising awareness about cancer prevention and detection. The organization offers a variety of services and programs to support individuals and families affected by cancer, including free lodging for cancer patients and caregivers traveling for treatment, a 24/7 helpline, and support groups. The ACS also provides information and resources related to cancer prevention and early detection, including guidelines for cancer screenings, healthy lifestyle choices, and ways to reduce cancer risk. The organization relies on donations and volunteer efforts to support its mission.

Website for Cancer Resources

Phone Number for Cancer Resources

American Heart Association

The American Heart Association (AHA) is a non-profit organization that promotes cardiovascular health and aims to reduce disability and deaths caused by cardiovascular diseases and stroke. It was founded in 1924 and is headquartered in Dallas, Texas, with over 3,400 employees and more than 33 million volunteers and supporters.

The AHA provides a variety of services and resources to promote cardiovascular health, including education, advocacy, research funding, community programs, and public health campaigns. They offer resources and programs for healthcare professionals, patients, and the general public, including information on heart disease prevention, healthy lifestyle choices, CPR and emergency cardiovascular care training, and research on cardiovascular disease.

The AHA also hosts several fundraising events, such as the Heart Walk and Go Red for Women, which raise money for research, education, and public health initiatives. They collaborate with other organizations, healthcare providers, and government agencies to promote cardiovascular health and improve patient outcomes.

Website for Heart Health Resources

_____

_____

Phone Number for Heart Health Resources

_____

_____

Disability Support

Disability support refers to various resources and services available to people with disabilities to help them live as independently as possible and participate fully in their communities. These services can include medical care, assistive technologies, vocational rehabilitation, and accommodations in the workplace or school.

Some examples of disability support organizations include the National Council on Independent Living, which advocates for the rights of people with disabilities, and the National Organization on Disability, which provides information and resources for people with disabilities and their families.

In addition, many countries have government-funded disability support programs, such as Social Security Disability Insurance (SSDI) in the United States, which provides financial assistance to people with disabilities who are unable to work.

Overall, disability support is designed to help people with disabilities overcome barriers and achieve their goals, whether those goals involve independent living, education, or employment.

Organization Name

_____

_____

Website for Disability Support Resources

_____

_____

Phone Number for Disability Support Resources

_____

_____

Elder Care

Elder care refers to the support and assistance provided to older adults who may require help with their daily activities due to physical, cognitive, or medical conditions. Elder care can include a range of services, including:

- **In-home care:** This may involve a caregiver coming to the senior's home to provide assistance with daily tasks such as bathing, dressing, meal preparation, and medication management.

- **Assisted living facilities:** These are residential facilities that provide housing, meals, housekeeping, transportation, and assistance with daily activities.

- **Nursing homes:** These are long-term care facilities that provide 24-hour medical care and assistance with daily activities for seniors who require more extensive care.

- **Adult day care:** This involves seniors spending the day at a facility where they can participate in social activities, receive meals and snacks, and receive assistance with daily tasks.

- **Hospice care:** This is end-of-life care that focuses on providing comfort and support to individuals who are terminally ill and their families.

Elder care may also include legal and financial planning, transportation services, and other support services that can help seniors maintain their independence and quality of life.

Organization Name

_____

_____

Website for Elder Care Resources

_____

_____

Phone Number for Elder Care Resources

_____

_____

National Alliance on Mental Illness (NAMI)

The National Alliance on Mental Illness (NAMI) is an American advocacy group that provides support, education, and resources for individuals and families affected by mental illness. NAMI offers programs and services such as support groups, education classes, advocacy, and helplines to help those affected by mental illness better understand their conditions and cope with the challenges they may face. NAMI also works to raise awareness and reduce the stigma surrounding mental illness, and advocates for policies and funding to improve mental health care and services.

Organization Name

_____

_____

Website for Mental Health Resources

_____

_____

Phone Number for Mental Health Resources

_____

_____

Legal Resources

Legal resources refer to organizations or entities that provide legal advice or assistance to individuals or businesses. They may offer free or low-cost legal services, advice, and information to help people understand their legal rights and responsibilities.

Some examples of legal resources include:

- **Legal aid organizations:** Nonprofit organizations that provide free or low-cost legal services to individuals and families who cannot afford an attorney. These organizations may specialize in certain areas of law, such as family law or immigration law.

- **Bar associations:** Organizations of licensed attorneys in a specific jurisdiction that provide legal resources, referrals, and support to both attorneys and the public.

- **Law clinics:** Law schools may operate clinics that provide legal services to the community under the supervision of law professors and licensed attorneys.

- **Self-help legal resources:** Online resources, books, and guides that provide information and guidance on legal issues for individuals who cannot afford or do not wish to hire an attorney.

- **Court-sponsored programs:** Some courts may offer programs such as legal assistance clinics or self-help centers to help individuals navigate the legal system and understand their rights.

- **Pro bono programs:** Many attorneys and law firms offer pro bono (free) legal services to individuals and organizations in need.

Law Firm

Firm Name

Contact Information

Legal Aid Organization

Organization Name

Contact Information

Notes

Financial Resources

Financial resources are tools, services, and organizations that can provide assistance with managing finances, such as budgeting, saving, investing, and obtaining credit. These resources can be especially useful for individuals or families facing financial challenges or looking to improve their financial well-being. Here are some examples of financial resources:

- **Financial Counseling:** Financial counseling is a service provided by many organizations that can help individuals develop a budget, manage debt, and plan for their financial future.

- **Non-Profit Credit Counseling:** Non-profit credit counseling organizations can provide financial education, debt management plans, and credit counseling services to help individuals manage their debt.

- **Financial Education Resources:** Financial education resources can include books, websites, and classes that provide information and guidance on financial topics.

- **Financial Planning Services:** Financial planning services can help individuals plan for their financial future, such as retirement planning, estate planning, and investment management.

- **Government Programs:** Government programs, such as the Federal Trade Commission (FTC) and the Consumer Financial Protection Bureau (CFPB), provide information and resources to help consumers with financial issues, such as identity theft, credit reporting, and debt collection.

- **Community Organizations:** Community organizations, such as churches, non-profit organizations, and local government agencies, can offer financial assistance to individuals in need.

- **Online Tools:** There are many online tools available to help individuals with budgeting, saving, investing, and managing their finances. These tools include budgeting apps, financial calculators, and investment tracking software.

- **Credit Monitoring Services:** Credit monitoring services can help individuals keep track of their credit report and monitor for any changes or suspicious activity.

- **Loan Services:** Loan services, such as banks, credit unions, and online lenders, can provide individuals with loans for various purposes, such as purchasing a home, starting a business, or paying off debt.

- **Investment Services:** Investment services, such as brokerage firms and financial advisors, can provide individuals with guidance and advice on investing their money.

Debt Management

Organization Name

Contact Information

Notes

Financial Assistance Program

Program Name

Contact Information

Notes

Community Resources

Community resources refer to various local organizations, agencies, and services that provide assistance to people in need. These resources can include food banks, homeless shelters, community centers, and public libraries, among others.

Food banks are a type of community resource that provides food assistance to people who are struggling with hunger. These organizations often rely on donations from individuals and businesses to provide food to those in need. Homeless shelters, on the other hand, provide temporary housing and support services to people who are experiencing homelessness. Community centers are places where people can gather for social and recreational activities, as well as educational and wellness programs. Public libraries are another valuable community resource that provide access to books, computers, and other educational resources.

In addition to these examples, there are many other community resources available that can help people in various ways. Some communities have organizations that provide legal assistance, job training programs, transportation services, and other types of support. These resources can be especially important for individuals and families who are facing financial or other challenges. It's always a good idea to research and familiarize yourself with the community resources available in your area so that you can access them if needed.

Local Support Group

Group Name

Contact Information

Community Center

_____

_____

Center Name

_____

_____

Contact Information

_____

_____

Notes

_____

_____

Emergency Resources

Emergency resources refer to the organizations, services, and individuals that provide immediate assistance in case of a crisis, disaster, or emergency situation. These resources include:

- **Emergency medical services (EMS):** EMS personnel respond to medical emergencies and provide life-saving interventions, such as CPR, defibrillation, and administering medications.

- **Fire and rescue services:** Firefighters and rescue workers respond to fires, accidents, and other emergencies, providing fire suppression, rescue, and other assistance.

- **Law enforcement agencies:** Law enforcement agencies such as police departments, sheriff's offices, and state troopers respond to emergencies involving criminal activity or public safety.

- **Disaster relief organizations:** Organizations such as the American Red Cross, Salvation Army, and FEMA provide aid to people affected by natural disasters such as hurricanes, floods, and earthquakes.

- **Emergency shelters:** Shelters provide a safe place to stay for people who are displaced due to disasters, homelessness, or other emergencies.

- **Poison control centers:** Poison control centers provide advice and assistance in case of poisoning emergencies.

- **Crisis hotlines:** Crisis hotlines provide confidential support and assistance to people in crisis, including suicide prevention and mental health services.

- **Utility companies:** Utility companies such as electricity, gas, and water providers have emergency response teams that can quickly restore service in case of outages or other emergencies.

It's important to have a list of emergency resources and their contact information readily available in case of an emergency.

Emergency Services

Service Name

Contact Information

Disaster Relief Organization

Organization Name

_____

_____

_____

Contact Information

_____

_____

_____

Shelter

Shelter refers to a place where someone can live, usually on a temporary basis, when they have nowhere else to go or cannot stay in their current home. Shelters can be run by government agencies, non-profit organizations, or other groups, and can offer a variety of services such as meals, clothing, and counseling in addition to housing. Shelters can provide temporary housing for people experiencing homelessness, victims of domestic violence or other crises, and people displaced by natural disasters or other emergencies. Some shelters may have specific requirements for entry, such as sobriety, while others may be open to anyone in need.

Shelter Name

_____

_____

_____

Contact Information

_____

_____

_____

Chapter 17:

TO-DO LIST

––––

The "To-Do List" section serves as a reminder to gather and organize important documents and records. These documents are essential for various purposes, such as identification, legal matters, financial planning, and estate management. Here's a breakdown of the list of documents and their possible locations:

List of Documents Needed:

- **Passport:** A travel document used for international travel and identification.

- **Driver's License:** A government-issued identification card for driving privileges.

- **Social Security Card:** An official document containing your unique Social Security number.

- **Birth Certificate:** A document that provides proof of your birth and identity.

- **Marriage Certificate:** A legal document that verifies a marriage between two individuals.

- **Divorce Decree:** A legal document that outlines the terms of a divorce settlement.

- **Will:** A legal document that outlines how your assets will be distributed after your death.

- **Trust:** A legal arrangement where a trustee manages assets on behalf of beneficiaries.

- **Power of Attorney:** A legal document that authorizes someone to act on your behalf in legal and financial matters.

- **Health Care Directives:** Legal documents that outline your wishes for medical treatment and end-of-life care.

- **Insurance Policies:** Documents related to life, health, auto, home, or other insurance coverage.

- **Retirement Account Information:** Documents related to your retirement accounts, such as 401(k) or IRA statements.

- **Investment Account Information:** Documents related to your investment accounts, such as brokerage or mutual fund statements.

- **Bank Account Information:** Details about your bank accounts, including account numbers and contact information.

- **Credit Card Information:** Details about your credit cards, including account numbers and contact information.

- **Tax Returns:** Copies of your tax returns for the last three years.

- **Property Deeds and Titles:** Documents that prove ownership of real estate or other properties.

- **Vehicle Registration:** Documents related to the registration and ownership of your vehicles.

- **Military Records (If Applicable):** Documents related to your military service, such as discharge papers or service records.

Location of Documents:

- **Home Safe or Lockbox:** Keep important documents in a secure safe or lockbox at your residence.

- **Bank Safety Deposit Box:** Rent a safety deposit box at a bank to store important documents.

- **Trusted Friend or Family Member's Home:** Entrust a close friend or family member with copies of important documents.

- **Lawyer's Office:** Store copies of legal documents at your lawyer's office for safekeeping.

- **Other:** Specify any other locations where you may have stored copies of important documents, such as a digital cloud storage service or a trusted advisor's office.

Remember to keep the originals and copies of these documents in a secure and easily accessible place, and inform trusted individuals about their location in case of emergencies or when they are needed.

Set Aside Time to Fill out Each Section of the Journal:

Date: _____

Time: _____

- Discuss and Make Decisions with Partner on Important Topics

Date of Discussion: _____

Topics Discussed: _____

_____

_____

_____

_____

_____

- Update as Needed with Changes in Personal Information or Circumstances

Date of Update: _____

Information Updated: _____

_____

_____

_____

_____

_____

- Keep in a Safe and Easily Accessible Location

Location: _____

_____

_____

- Periodically Review and Update Information as Necessary

Date of Review: _____

Information Updated: _____

_____

_____

- Inform Trusted Loved Ones or Executor of the Existence and
  Location of the Journal

Name of Individual Informed: _____

Relationship to Couple: _____

Name of Individual Informed: _____

Relationship to Couple: _____

Name of Individual Informed: _____

Relationship to Couple: _____

Name of Individual Informed: _____

Relationship to Couple: _____

Name of Individual Informed: _____

Relationship to Couple: _____

Name of Individual Informed: _____

Relationship to Couple: _____

Name of Individual Informed: _____

Chapter 18:

THOUGHTS & FINAL WISHES

––––

T he "Thoughts & Final Wishes" section provides an opportunity for you to express your personal thoughts, reflections, and final wishes for the future. It allows you to share your desires, beliefs, and values with your loved ones and those responsible for carrying out your wishes after you're gone. Here are some key aspects to consider:

- **Personal Thoughts:** This section can include any personal reflections, messages, or sentiments you want to convey to your loved ones. It may include messages of love, gratitude, or advice that you want to leave behind.

- **Inspirations:** You can share your sources of inspiration, such as quotes, poems, or books that have influenced you. These can serve as guidance and inspiration for your family and friends.

- **Final Wishes:** This section is an opportunity to express your wishes for your funeral or memorial service. You can specify whether you prefer a burial or cremation, the type of ceremony you would like, and any specific requests regarding music, readings, or rituals.

- **Legacy and Charitable Contributions:** If you have specific wishes for how you want to be remembered or if you want to make charitable contributions in your name, you can include those details here. This can involve specifying organizations or causes that are meaningful to you.

- **Digital Assets and Online Presence:** With the increasing digital presence in our lives, you may want to address your digital assets, such as social media accounts, email accounts, and digital files. You can provide instructions on how you want these assets to be handled or if you want them to be preserved or deleted.

It's important to regularly review and update this section to ensure your thoughts and wishes accurately reflect your current mindset and intentions. Consider discussing these matters with your loved ones, legal advisors, or estate planners to ensure that your wishes are known and can be properly carried out when the time comes.

This section is for you to record any personal thoughts, inspirations, and wishes for the future. It's an opportunity to reflect on your life together and document your aspirations for the years to come.

Here are Some Prompts to get Started:

Type of Service Desired

Religious: _____

Secular: _____

Other: _____

Burial or Cremation

Burial: _____

Cremation: _____

Cemetery or

Final Resting Place: _____

Phone: _____

eMail: _____

Relationship: _____

Other Important Details: _____

Special Requests or Traditions

Music: _____

Readings: _____

Poems: _____

Flowers: _____

Charitiable Donations: _____

Other: _____

Preferred Funeral Home: _____

Contact Information: _____

Name: _____

Address: _____

City: _____

State: _____ Zip Code: _____

Country: _____

Phone: _____

eMail: _____

Notes: _____

End of Life Care

Preferred Medical Facility: _____

Facility Contact Information: _____

Advanced Directive: _____

Living Will: _____

Do Not Resuscitate

(DNR) Orders: _____

Hospice or Palliative

Care Preferences: _____

Other Important Details: _____

Memorial Service or Celebration of Life Preferences

Preferred Date: _____

Preferred Time: _____

Theme or Tone of Service: _____

Music to be Included: _____

Readings to be Included: _____

Special Requests or
Traditions: _____

Other Important Details: _____

Preferred Obituary Information

Name: _____

Age: _____

Residence at Time of
Passing: _____

Date of Death: _____

Cause of Death: _____

Surviving Family: _____

Preferred Charities: _____

Special Accomplishments
Or Achievements: _____

Charitable Organizations to be Notified

Name of Organization: _____

Contact Information: _____

Preferred Donation Type: _____

Preferred Donation Amount: _____

Name of Organization: _____

Contact Information: _____

Preferred Donation Type: _____

Preferred Donation Amount: _____

Personal Items to be Distributed or Passed Down

The section on "Personal Items to be Distributed or Passed Down" allows you to specify the personal belongings that you wish to distribute among your loved ones or pass down as heirlooms. These items hold sentimental value and can carry memories and stories that you want to preserve within your family. Here are some considerations for this section:

- **List of Items:** Create a detailed list of personal items that you want to distribute or pass down. These items can include jewelry, artwork, furniture, family heirlooms, photographs, sentimental objects, collections, or any other possessions that hold personal significance to you.

- **Recipients:** Indicate the names of the individuals whom you wish to receive each specific item. This can include family members, friends, or other loved ones. Be as specific as possible to avoid confusion or potential disputes.

- **Instructions:** If you have any specific instructions or wishes regarding the distribution or preservation of certain items, make sure to include them. For example, you may want to specify that a particular piece of jewelry should be given to a specific family member on a special occasion, or that a certain artwork should be displayed in a particular location.

- **Legacy Letters:** Consider writing personal letters to accompany certain items. These letters can explain the significance of the item, share memories associated with it, or express your hopes for its future preservation. This can provide a deeper understanding and connection to the item for the recipient.

- **Executor or Trustee:** If you have designated an executor or trustee to handle your estate, ensure that they are aware of your wishes regarding the distribution of personal items. Provide them with a copy of this section to ensure that your instructions are followed.

Remember to periodically review and update this section as your preferences may change over time. Open communication with your loved ones about your intentions and the significance of these items can also help to ensure a smooth and respectful distribution process.

List of Items to be Given and Who They Should be Given to:

_____

_____

_____

_____

_____

Instructions on How to Distribute Items:

_____

_____

_____

_____

Special Requests or Conditions for Certain Items:

_____

_____

Other Final Wishes or Instructions:

_____

_____

_____

CONCLUSION

———

In conclusion, this journal serves as a comprehensive guide and record-keeping tool for important personal information and end-of-life wishes. It is important to keep one's affairs in order to ensure that loved ones are not burdened with difficult decisions during an already emotional and challenging time.

Remember to update the journal regularly as personal information and circumstances change. Keep the journal in a safe and easily accessible location, and inform trusted loved ones or executor of its existence and location.

It is recommended to review and update the information in the journal periodically, to ensure it remains up-to-date and accurate.

Reflection on the importance of completing this journal:

_____

_____

By completing this journal, we are taking a proactive step towards ensuring that our affairs are in order and that our loved ones are not left with the burden of difficult decisions. It provides peace of mind to know that our end-of-life wishes are recorded and can be easily accessed when needed.

We encourage our loved ones to also complete a journal like this, as it is a valuable tool for anyone to have. Let us all take responsibility for our affairs and plan for the future.

The final section of the journal serves as a concluding statement emphasizing the importance of completing the journal and keeping one's affairs in order. Here's a breakdown of the key points:

- **Comprehensive Guide and Record-Keeping:** The journal serves as a comprehensive guide and record-keeping tool for important personal information and end-of-life wishes. It provides a centralized location to document and organize critical details, ensuring that nothing is overlooked.

- **Lightening the Burden:** By completing the journal, you alleviate the burden on your loved ones during an already emotional and challenging time. It allows them to have access to essential information and instructions, minimizing the stress and confusion associated with decision-making.

- **Regular Updates:** It is crucial to update the journal regularly as personal information and circumstances change. Life events, such as births, deaths, marriages, or divorces, may necessitate revisions to ensure accuracy and relevance.

- **Safe and Accessible Location:** Keep the journal in a safe and easily accessible location. Inform trusted loved ones or your designated executor about its existence and where to find it. This ensures that the information can be promptly accessed when needed.

- **Review and Update:** It is recommended to review and update the information in the journal periodically. Set aside time annually or as significant changes occur to ensure that the details remain current and reflect your current wishes and circumstances.

- **Encouraging Others:** Reflect on the importance of completing this journal and encourage your loved ones to do the same. Stress that this tool is valuable for anyone to have, regardless of age or health status. By taking responsibility for our affairs and planning for the future, we empower ourselves and provide peace of mind to those we care about.

Completing this journal is a proactive and responsible step towards ensuring your wishes are known and your loved ones are supported. It allows you to take control of your affairs and provides reassurance that your intentions will be honored.

Person 1

Name: _____

Date: _____

Signature: _____

Person 2

Name: _____

Date: _____

Signature: _____

Printed in Great Britain
by Amazon

43781751R00156